puzzling escapes

Trapped in the Bookstore

Beth Mar[illegible]

BethMartinBooks.com

Cover by Beth Martin. Bookshelf and pile of open books image from Elena Schweitzer/Shutterstock.com

ISBN 978-1-952688-02-7

Beth Martin Books
P.O. Box 2191
Columbia, MD 21045

BethMartinBooks.com

To every book lover and
escape room enthusiast.
Good luck.

AN UNPLEASANT SURPRISE

David has been acting strangely all day, but you have a good idea why. "You're trying to keep me busy while our friends set up a surprise party for my birthday, aren't you?" you ask.

He shakes his head. "No. Only seven-year-olds have surprise parties."

You laugh. David is probably the smartest person you know, but he's terrible at keeping secrets. "So is this really how we're going to celebrate?" you ask, gesturing at the street around you, which is in the historical area of town. "Browsing old stuffy stores covered in dust?"

Before your friend can respond, it starts to downpour. Both of you forgot to bring an umbrella, so you dash under the closest awning, which happens to be in front of a bookstore.

"Ugh, this is just my luck," you groan. "I wish we could do something a little more exciting on my birthday."

In just the few seconds the two of you were in the rain, you both got soaked. Water is dripping from David's shaggy blond hair and the tip of his nose, and his teeshirt clings to his shoulders. "Why don't we go to an arcade or bowling alley once the rain dies down a bit?" he suggests. "Oh! I heard there's a new escape room just a couple blocks from here. Why don't we do that?"

You scratch your chin as you consider his suggestion. "That sounds good. Hopefully this storm blows over quickly. In the meantime, why don't we go inside?"

"Sure." David walks up to the door, which has a sign above it saying *Athena Booksellers*. "This is actually my favorite store in the entire historic square." He pushes the door open and you follow him inside. There's no one at the register, but you see a couple of people browsing the new-release books displayed at the front. "I might check if they have any of Sanderson's books I haven't read yet."

The two of you walk to the back corner of the store, where the fiction books are located. As your friend carefully scans the books, looking for something by his favorite author, you grab the first book you see and start reading it.

"It doesn't seem like they have anything new," he says.

"Was it not at the front of the store with the other new books?"

"Let me check."

You return the book you were holding to its spot on the shelf and walk over to the front of the store. David adjusts his backpack and says, "I hope they have something I haven't read yet."

As you approach the new releases, you realize the selection is quite small.

"What's that on the door?" David asks. When he gets to the front entrance, he looks at a sign hanging in the window, then pushes firmly against the door handle. It makes the string of bells attached jingle loudly, but the door doesn't open. He pushes again, the bells protesting in another brassy clatter.

"Wait," you say, stepping up to the door. You notice something around the handle, in addition to the rope holding the bells. There's a chain with a lock holding the door shut. "We're locked in."

"This isn't good," he says, shaking his head. "They weren't supposed to close for another fifteen minutes. Surely the owner is around here somewhere and can let us out." You look around and are confident that you and David are the only ones in the store.

A sudden bolt of lightning closely followed by a boom of thunder makes both of you jump. The storm is getting pretty intense, and you're glad—at least for the moment—that you're inside. "What's this?" you ask, pulling the sign out of the window.

You start to panic. "They're closed? Forever?" It doesn't make sense that the store would lock up so suddenly, especially with you and your friend still inside. The last thing you wanted to do for your birthday was wait for the owner to return to let you out, especially if the store won't be opening again. You reach into your pocket and grab your phone, but when you press the power button, the screenremains black. "Shoot, it's dead."

David searches through his bag in a fury. "I left my phone in my car! What are we going to do?"

You look closer at the lock and chain. "Well, it requires a combination. Maybe there's a clue somewhere in here as to what that combination might be."

"Right," David agrees. "Let's look around and see what we can find."

HOW TO USE THIS BOOK

Inspired by the rising popularity of escape rooms, *Puzzling Escapes: Trapped in a Bookstore* locks you inside an independent bookstore after closing time. As you read this book, you'll need to collect clues and solve puzzles in order to advance through the story and hopefully escape the building. You'll be accompanied by your friend David, who will be able to help whenever you get stuck on a puzzle or can't figure out a particular code.

There is not a strict time limit for completing the book. However, if you would like the added pressure of a ticking clock, feel free to set a timer. Two hours would be a good goal for a seasoned puzzle solver. You will want a pencil or pen to take notes. Scissors may be useful but are not required. No outside resources are needed to complete this book, and you won't need an internet connection to check your answers.

This book is divided into several sections. The first three—main floor, second floor, and employees only—are the three areas of the bookstore and are where you'll encounter most of the puzzles. Your adventure will start on the main floor. Be sure not to move on to the second floor and employees only area until instructed to do so.

Each puzzle has a unique keyword that you'll use to look up hints and solutions, check your answers, and find out what happens next. The answer to each puzzle will be a three-digit number from 000 to 999.

The next sections are as follows:

HINTS

If you get stuck on a puzzle and aren't sure how to begin, ask your friend David what he thinks. The hints are listed alphabetically by keyword and won't include the titles of the puzzles. Only read the section for the puzzle you're currently working on so you don't spoil any of the fun! David will list any clues that you should have for the current puzzle and give you an idea of how to proceed.

SOLUTIONS

In case you aren't able to complete a certain puzzle, you can ask David to solve it for you. He will tell you what the answer is and explain how he got it. Always read the hint for a puzzle before going to the solution since it's possible you're missing a clue. The solutions are also listed in alphabetical order by keyword. After reading a solution, you may continue directly to the conclusion section.

CONCLUSION

Once you and David have solved a puzzle, find out what happens next by reading the entry for that puzzle in the conclusion section. Never skip the conclusion, because you might find objects and clues for other puzzles.

ANSWER CHECK

When you think you know the answer to a puzzle, you'll want to make sure it's correct before continuing. There is a two-part check for your answer. First, find your three-digit answer in the number table to get a cell address. Then in the keyword table, find the cell for the address you received. If the word in the cell is the keyword for the puzzle you solved, your answer is correct. Otherwise, you should try again—and use a hint or read the solution if you get really stuck.

For example, if you're working on a puzzle that has the keyword "weight" and you believe the answer is 123, then find 123 in the number table of the check section (go ahead, do it). Next to 123 in the number table is the cell address A6. Flip to the keyword table and see what word is in the A row and the 6th column (do this too). That cell contains the word "weight," which means 123 was the correct answer for this example.

Please don't try to reverse lookup an answer using the check section—instead, find the answers for any puzzles you can't solve in the solutions section.

If you have access to the internet, you can also check your answer by inputting the keyword and answer into the website: check.BethMartinBooks.com

OBJECTS

As you read the conclusions to each segment, you'll find a variety of objects. When you read "You find ____" anywhere in the text, that means there's an object in the object section with that specific name. Simply tear each one out as you find it so you can keep each clue you've collected in hand.

DAVID'S BACKPACK

You're in a bookstore, so you have access to all kinds of books! David has selected a few and placed them in his backpack for easy reference.

You may now continue to the main floor.

Main Floor

Second Floor

Employees Only

Hints

Solutions

Conclusion

Answer Check

Objects

Main Floor

MAIN FLOOR

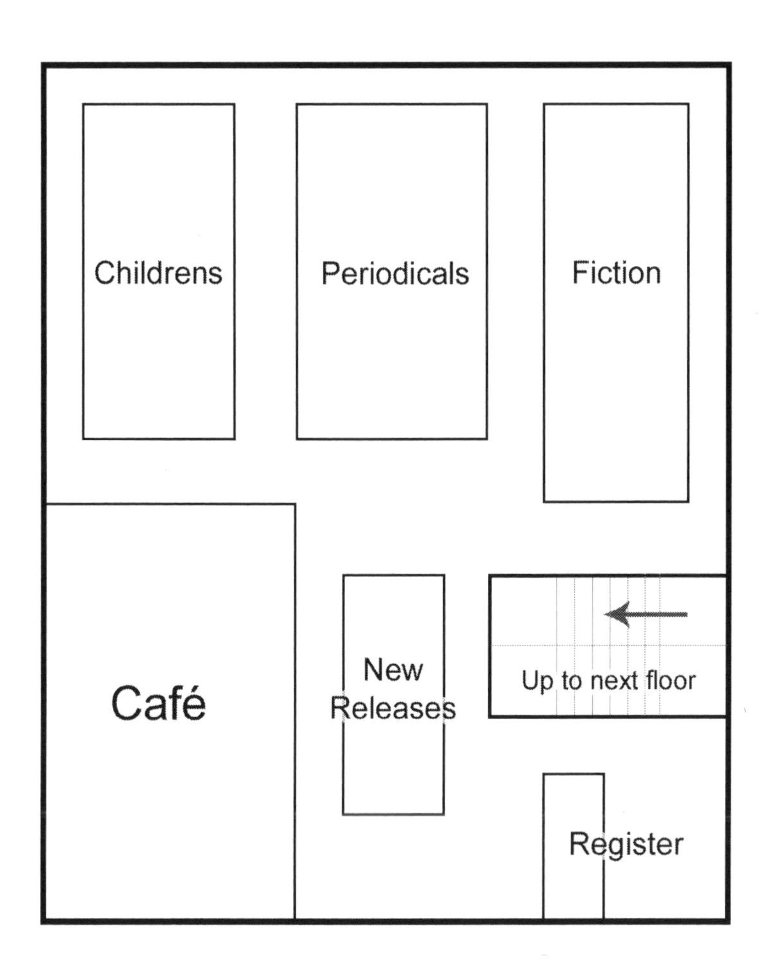
Childrens
Periodicals
Fiction
Café
New Releases
Up to next floor
Register

LOOK AROUND

Even with the lights still on, the main area of the bookstore isn't well-lit. The store has a strong smell—a mix of the woody scent of the old floorboards, the aroma of coffee beans from the café, and the hint of mildew that tends to come with age.

For an independent bookshop, the interior appears quite orderly. All the books are aligned on towering, black metal shelves or arranged in neat stacks on darkly stained wooden tables. Although the sections are clearly marked, the books within each one aren't organized particularly well. When you stand at the new-releases table, the checkout counter is to your right. A fancy new tablet that serves as a register is mounted on an antique wooden desk.

To your left is a small café. Behind a wooden bar is an impressive-looking, polished-copper espresso machine. The

brick wall in back of the machine has a few open shelves holding a multitude of white porcelain mugs and a trio of cabinets. The café area has a few tables and chairs where you've seen freelancers working by day and university students studying in the evenings.

The back half of the store is divided into three sections: the children's books, magazines and periodicals, and fiction.

Next to the register is a walled-off section which holds the staircase to the mezzanine, where the non-fiction books and restrooms are located. For a small store, it feels quite spacious since the café is open to the second floor. The metal support beams are exposed, giving the space an industrial feel.

To be honest, you've enjoyed browsing the bookstore in the past, and you're sad that it's closed. However, you're more upset about being locked inside. You resolve to look around for clues so you and David can get out.

REGISTER

Keyword: bike

In such an old store, you expected an antique register with mechanical buttons and maybe even a little bell that dings when the cash drawer opens. Instead, the antique desk which serves as the checkout stand holds a white tablet that swivels to face either the cashier or customer. The cashbox, however, is a locked drawer on the desk with no frills, just a combination lock.

"The owner was pretty savvy with the times," David says as he pokes at the tablet. The screen turns on, asking for a username. "This place is usually pretty busy. I wonder why it closed."

"I don't know," you respond. "But I'm more interested in getting out of here. Do you think the combination to the front door might be in the cash drawer?"

"Doubtful, but it's worth a try. I'm guessing it's saved on here." He types the word *admin* into the tablet, which then prompts him to enter a password. "Any guesses?"

You shrug. There must be something you're missing. You check through each drawer of the desk, finding all sorts of odds and ends including pens, paperclips, receipt paper, and a stash of plastic bags. Finally, in the bottom drawer, you spot a small notepad that has writing on the top page. You rip it off and show it to David.

"Hey, that looks like it might be a clue. Let's figure out what it means."

CoDeX fIX

FICTION

Keyword: finish

In the depths of the bookstore lies the grid of shelves which make up the fiction section. The organization here is seriously lacking. There are no separate shelves for different genres. Instead, the books are crammed together, placed almost at random. They aren't even ordered by the author's names. No wonder it was so hard to find things in this shop.

But what interests you more than the disorganized shelves is a locked display case mounted on the back wall. Through the glass, you can see a number of old books. You wouldn't mind owning one of them and say so to David.

"I don't think those will help us," he says.

"There could be another clue or puzzle tucked inside of one of them," you point out.

"True. Let's see if we can find the combination to open up that lock."

PERIODICALS

Keyword: effect

Against the back wall is a tall set of shelves holding all the magazines and other periodicals. David is immediately drawn to the latest issue of Logic Problems Monthly. You glance at the wide selection of interests including fashion, decorating, cars, crafts, world news, and science. There are trashy tabloids and thick literary magazines all grouped together, waiting to be read.

You don't want to waste time perusing, but one of the colorful covers catches your eye. You reach out to grab the magazine; however, David interrupts you, saying, "This is interesting. Come check it out."

You abandon the flashy cover and walk up to his side. "What's up?"

"I found a page tucked inside this puzzle magazine. It's the same type of logic puzzle as the ones printed in the magazine, but different." You look at the puzzle in his right hand. It's on clean, white paper, whereas the magazine it came from is printed on thin, grayish newsprint paper. Even the size of the puzzle and style of letters are different.

"What type of puzzle is it?"

"A nonogram. Each row and column has a list of numbers which corresponds to how many black squares are in that set. Like, this top row has 1 3, which means there's a single black square and a string of three consecutive black squares in the row. The rest have to be white. What we don't know is how many of those white squares come before the first black square, between the single black square and set of three, and after the last black square. There must be at least one white square between the sets of one and three, but there could also be more."

More interesting than the puzzle itself is the title. "*Decoder for Upper-Level Key*. You think the solution for this puzzle will unlock the stairs to the second level?"

"I hope so. Let's give it a shot."

You find Decoder for Upper-Level Key.

KIDS

Keyword: damage

You make your way past the café to the children's section. The shelves elsewhere are minimal black structures, but here, everything is colorful and fun. The children's shelves are arranged around a central red square rug, which holds a low table covered in blocks. There are a number of picture books and toys on display. Everything looks to be in place except for a single book on the table.

When you grab the book with the intention of putting it on the shelf, you notice there's a bookmark between two of the pages. You flip it open to find a drawing of a sleeping kitten and a poem.

Lazy little kittens,
Are sitting in a square,
So their purrs can rev,
Totally without care.

Lively puppy soon,
Enters and yells, "Yo!"
Troubling poor kitten,
Tripping on its toe.

Every kitty pet,
Roars a mighty meow,
Sounding in an echo.

"That's weird," David says when you show him the bookmarked page. "It's not finished."

You look again at the poem, then flip the page to check if there is more, but the following spread is another illustration and a new poem. The first two stanzas of the kitten poem each have four lines, with the second and fourth line rhyming, but the third stanza only has three lines and no rhyme. "You're right. Do you think we need to figure out what the last line is?" You try to think of words that rhyme with meow. Pow, chow, cow...

"Perhaps. But there also might be some other information hidden somehow."

You hold on to the book as you continue to look around the children's section. You see a lot of classic picture books from your childhood mixed in with a host of new titles. There's even a display of several books by a local author with a sign announcing an upcoming event where the author will be at the bookstore.

Another book catches your eye. It's titled, *365 Activities for Curious Boys and Girls*, and it sits among the study aids and test prep books. The cover of the book has begun to curl, and you assume someone has taken a great deal of time flipping through this particular book.

You highly suspect that whatever clue you get from the picture book will correspond with one of the activities inside.

CAFÉ

Keyword: noise

The front left half of the building was recently renovated into a sleek café. There are a few tables and chairs made from industrial-style black pipe and reclaimed wood. Although the rest of the bookstore has the original wood flooring, this area is covered in smooth dark tiles. The café is open to the second floor, and you notice the old building has impressively high ceilings. During the day, the two stories of front windows flood the front of the store with light. Now that it's late, the several little lamps hanging from above give the otherwise inviting area a stark glow.

A flash of lightning illuminates the street outside, and a second later, the loud clap of thunder shakes you to your core. The rain outside picks up, beating against the two stories of glass. For a moment, you wonder how strong the century-old windows are. You decide you're definitely safer inside the bookstore than if you were stranded outside.

David pokes around behind the counter. "All of the cabinets are locked."

"They probably only have coffee beans and mugs inside," you say.

He shrugs and walks over to a large copper machine. "We should still try to open them. What do you think this is?"

"Maybe it's for roasting the coffee beans," you suggest. You've never seen anything quite like it. Next to it is a shelf full of measuring cups that are connected with tubes and big containers. Something in the largest bowl catches your eye—a rubber duck with a large keyring attached.

"Hey, David. I think I found the keys for the cabinets!"

He joins your side and peers in. "How do we get it out? We can't reach inside."

You point to the measuring cup at the very top. "That one isn't covered, so we can pour water into it. The water will flow down the pipes and eventually make it to the bottom, fill it up, and bring the duck to the top. Then we can grab it and get the keys."

"All right. There's an extra pitcher to measure water here. Let's make sure to add exactly the right amount. I don't want to make the system overflow and end up with a huge mess."

"Right. Let's figure out exactly how many liters of water we need."

Your answer will be in the format of _ . _ _ L.

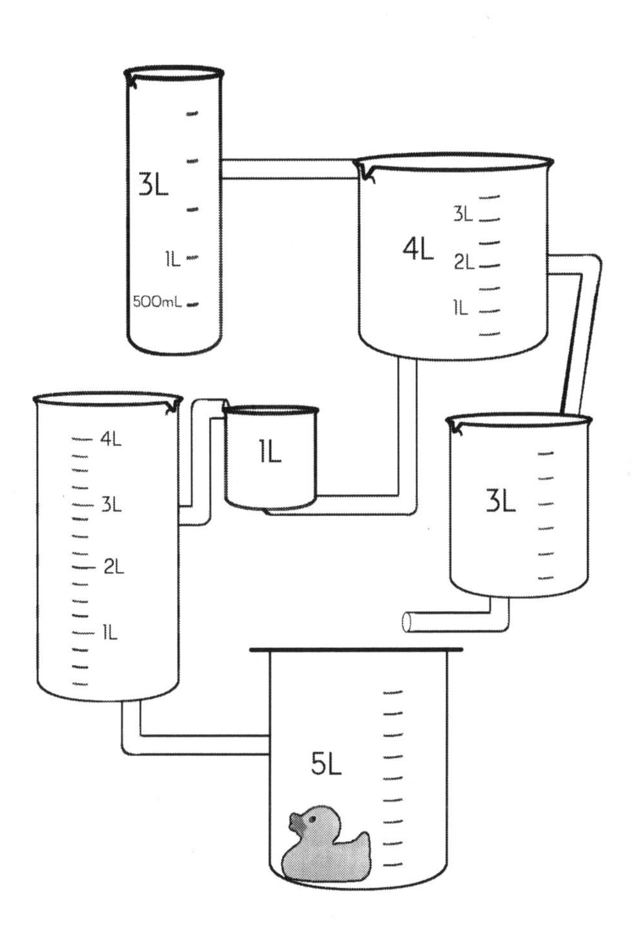
3L
1L
500mL
4L
3L
2L
1L
4L
3L
2L
1L
1L
3L
5L

NEW RELEASES

Keyword: knife

When you entered the bookstore, the first thing you came across was a large display of new releases and best-selling books. You revisit the two shelves and take a closer look at the selection. The shelf facing the door displays a wide array

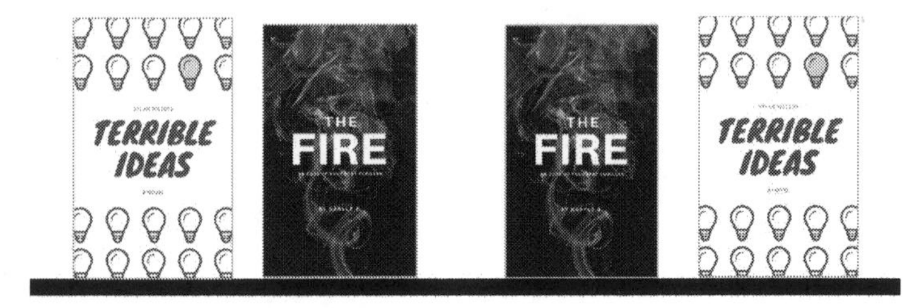

of novels and non-fiction books. However, the other shelf only contains two titles.

You pick up on of the many copies of *Terrible Ideas* and give it a closer look.

"I've been meaning to read that one," David says as he suddenly walks up next to you. "The author had a signing here when it first released. I guess she's related to the owner."

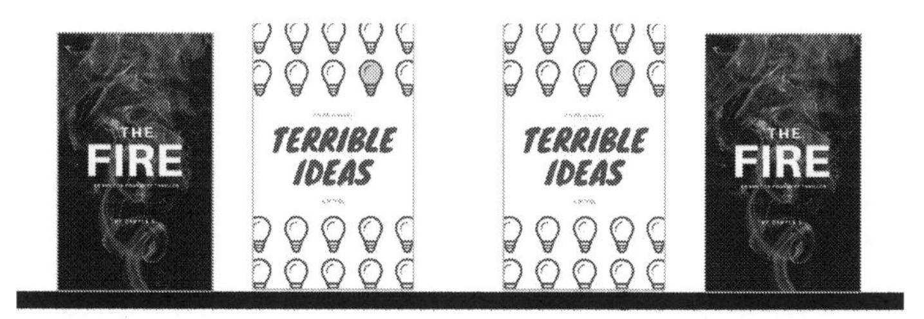

"That's cool," you say as you replace the book on the shelf. "That would explain why there are so many copies of it here. What about this other book?"

David takes a copy of *The Fire* and glances at the back. "Never heard of this one before. Looks like it might be interesting." He puts the book back, then moves to the next table. "I will never understand why bookstores sell non-book stuff."

You join him next to the table. There are a number of tote bags, pencil cases, and stationary displayed on top and in baskets underneath. "It all seems bookish enough." One bag in particular catches your attention. It's printed with a quote from *Alice in Wonderland* and has a zipper closing the top. However, something is looped through the zipper pull and side of the bag, preventing you from opening it. "Hey, look at this. This bag has a lock on it."

David takes the bag from you. "Huh. I wonder if there's anything inside. It doesn't feel heavy. Still, we should try to open it."

He places the bag back on the table as you say, "I agree."

STAIRS TO SECOND FLOOR

Keyword: nuance

There's a walled-off area next to the register which must contain the stairs leading up to the mezzanine. You're not sure there's any reason to go up there, but you have been doing a ton of searching on the main floor and still haven't figured out the combination to the front door. There could be a clue on the second level.

During business hours, the door to the upper floor would be propped open so customers could go up and browse the collection. In fact, you're surprised the door would ever be locked. The keypad next to the door looks fairly new.

"We need to get upstairs," you announce, mostly to yourself.

David overhears you from the new-release table where he's been poking around and adds, "Yes. There's an employees only area. If there's a hint for the entrance lock, I bet it's inside that room."

"Yeah," you say in agreement before you continue looking around.

Don't continue to the second floor until you are instructed to do so.

Second
Floor

SECOND FLOOR

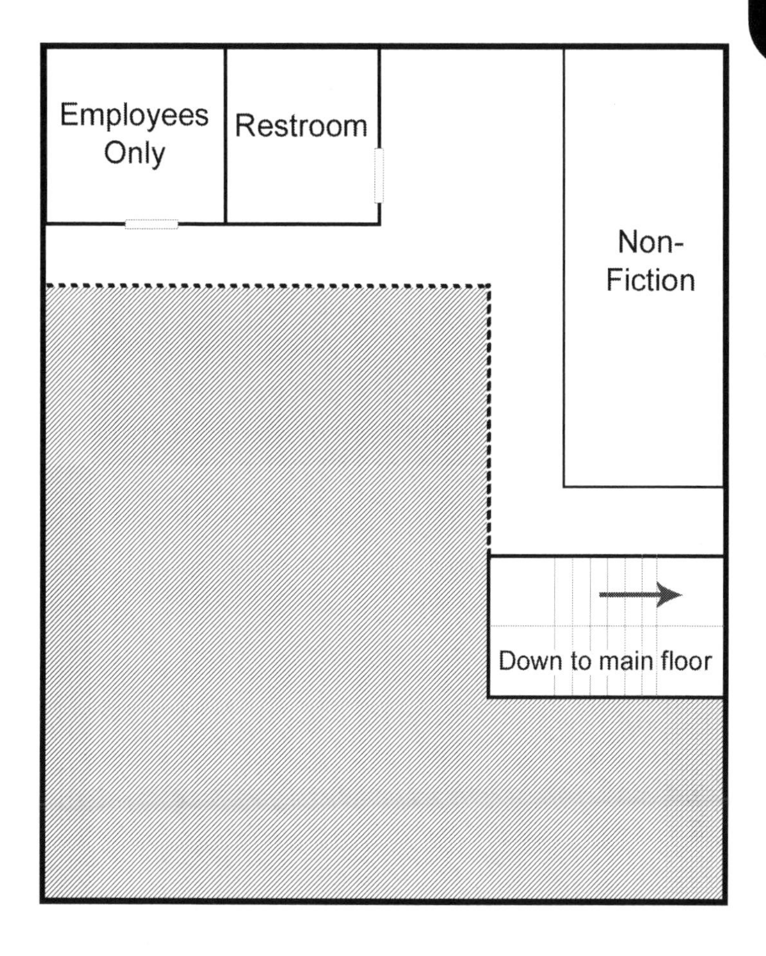

LOOK AROUND

You follow David up the stairs. The steps are steep and groan under your weight, but they feel sturdy enough. Once you get to the top, there's an open doorway out to the mezzanine. The view of the second floor from below was cool, but the vantage up here is even better. You approach the railing and look down at the main floor below. You can see the entire café and front of the building. A bolt of lightning flashes, briefly filling the store in bright light, then a crack of thunder shakes through the air a second later.

"It's really storming now," David observes. You can barely hear him over the sound of the rain pounding against the roof. "I normally enjoy thunderstorms, but I'm not sure this old building can take this kind of weather."

"It has been here for almost a hundred years—" You stop short as you step on a wet spot. Glancing up, you see that there is water dripping from one of the rafters above.

"The roof is leaking."

"I'll grab a bucket." David dashes ahead to the restrooms at the other end of the second floor. He returns with a yellow bucket on wheels and places it at the center of the puddle. A few seconds later, a water drop falls into the bucket with a satisfying plop. "All right. Now let's look around."

All of the non-fiction books are grouped together on the shelves. Political books are next to history, computer science, gardening, and self-help. Even though the books aren't categorized, everything is neatly arranged and the titles seem to be current. As you walk farther into the mezzanine, the floor seems to sag under the weight of the books. The restroom doesn't take the full width of the second floor, and you follow the narrow walkway around until you reach one last door, which has a sign saying 'employees only.' The door has one of those metal keypads that requires a passcode before the door will unlock.

You walk back over to the books on this floor and find David already looking around for clues.

NON-FICTION

Keyword: carbon

You grab the first computer book you see off the shelf and flip through it, then place it back on the shelf. All the books are crammed together, spine out. "Hey, come check this out," David says. You follow him to the side of the bookcases, where each one has a paper sign attached to it.

"The rows are labeled," you observe. "Too bad the books aren't arranged according to the signs."

"Doesn't that strike you as odd?"

You're about to remark that none of this store has been particularly organized, but then again, none of the areas had signs grouping the subsections. And when you look closer at the signs, something about them seems off. "Yeah, it does."

"And then there's this." He leads you down the row between the first and second signs. One of the shelves holds what looks like a large metal cash box with a small lock on it.

"Clearly we need to open that," you say.

RESTROOM

Keyword: convict

There is only a single restroom, and you decide to check it out. When you turn on the light, you notice the inside of this space is much newer than the rest of the building, so the bathroom must have been a recent addition. There's a toilet with a sink next to it and a simple mirror. The only other object in the room is a cabinet with glass panes on the doors. The fixture holds extra hand towels and toilet paper along with a strange statue. There's a lock keeping the cabinet doors shut.

You want to get that figure from inside, but you aren't sure where to find a code. As you turn to leave, you notice a sign above the lightswitch.

> A child finds a row of 1000 switches, all in the off position. He runs down the line and turns every switch on. Then, starting at the beginning, he flips every second switch. Then, he flips every third switch. He continues down the line, flipping every nth switch on his nth pass until he flips only the 1000th switch on his 1000th run down the line. Once he's done, what is the highest numbered switch in the "on" position?

LOCKED EMPLOYEES ONLY DOOR

Keyword: deep

You take the narrow walkway which passes the restroom and dead-ends at the back corner of the store. There's a sturdy door with an 'Employees Only' sign on it. You noticed the metal keypad next to it when you first came up to the second floor.

David approaches while you examine the keypad. "Do you think we'll need to get in there?" he asks.

"Probably." You were hoping to find some sort of clue on or around the door, but the keypad buttons are all evenly worn, and no detail of the door really strikes you as remarkable.

"I'm going to keep looking around this floor," David says.

Don't continue to the employees only room until you are instructed to do so.

Employees
Only

LOOK AROUND

Keyword: posture

The inside of the room is completely dark, and you have to feel around for a moment to find the light switch. You flick it on, and after a few seconds, a single lightbulb in the middle of the room begins to glow. The tiny room is crammed with extra inventory, books piled in every corner and available space. What could have been a table for staff to use during their lunch break is now a tower of science fiction and mystery books. The cabinet, which probably could have held a microwave, is instead heaped high with bookmarks, pens, and fancy journals.

"Not much of a break room," you remark.

"I've only seen the owner and his son working here," David says as he takes a tentative step into the room. "I'm not sure either of them ever take a break while at work. That, and who wants to take a break here when there's the café?"

You shake your head. "I'd hate for customers to inter-

rupt my lunch, thinking I'm always available."

David makes his way into the room and begins looking through the books on the table. "It's never too busy here in the middle of the day. I doubt they're ever hurting for breaks."

"Maybe," you say. But more important than the utility of this room for employee breaks is your desire to leave the store. You keep an eye out for anything that might be a clue.

"Hey, look at this." David pulls a piece of paper out from between the pages of a mystery book on top of the table. "It looks kind of wonky. I bet it's a clue."

You hold out your hand and say, "Let me see."

You must blurt out the message!

Hints

"What are we supposed to do with this?" you ask as David pores over the strange puzzle.

"Let's try just plugging everything in a calculator," he suggests as he pulls off his backpack. He rifles through it for a moment before pulling out a scientific calculator. "Let's see. If I put it all in I get... forty thousand, seven hundred two, and seventy-eight thousandths."

You hold out your hand and he gives you the calculator. The screen displays several more digits after the decimal than David said. "This number doesn't make any sense. Clearly we're missing something. What about the title of the puzzle?"

"Poorly translated book titles. I'm not familiar with any books that have these numbers in the titles... unless we need to translate them." He smiles broadly and you suspect he's figured out how to solve the puzzle. "The units. We need to convert them all into different units. Like 96,561 kilometers is"—he takes his calculator back and furiously punches in some numbers—"sixty thousand miles."

You raise your brows, skeptical of his idea. "I don't know of any books with sixty thousand miles in the title."

"No, neither do I. However, three miles is one league."

Suddenly, you understand what he's getting at. "*20,000 Leagues Under the Sea*! That's brilliant! The units are even in the title."

"Right. So now we just need to figure out the rest of them."

BIKE

No matter how long you stare at the note, nothing seems to come to you.

"I'm stumped," David admits. "Although..." He picks up the note and holds it close to his face. "What if we just ignore the lowercase letters? Can we get a number somehow by combining all the capitalized letters?"

CARBON

David sets his backpack on one of the shelves, then opens it and digs through the contents. "There it is," he says as he pulls out a pocket-sized book.

"A dictionary?" you ask. "Shouldn't there be a bigger one with more words somewhere around here?"

He's already flipping through the pages, studying them. "Probably."

"I'll go get one." You search around the non-fiction section, looking for the biggest book. You easily spot a dictionary, pull it out, start to page through, and find the meanings

of the words posted at the ends of the rows.

"None of them are in mine," David says from behind you.

You read off the definitions as you find them. "*Runology* is the study of runic alphabets, *scincoid* is some kind of lizard, and an *endoscope* is a tool for looking inside organs."

"Those are incredibly specific. Maybe we don't need their meaning, but the actual letters."

You idly scratch your head. "Maybe there are numbers hidden within the letters."

"I agree. But I don't think they're in English."

COMEDY

You will need to solve the signs in the non-fiction area for the second piece of this puzzle. If you need another hint when you have both pieces, look up the keyword give. The solution and conclusion will still be under the keyword comedy.

CONVICT

You show David the riddle inside the bathroom. "What do you think?" you ask.

David reads the sign, then says, "Huh. Well, it's too complex to try to actually simulate a thousand switches ourselves."

"Right. So what do we do?"

He scratches his chin. "What if we consider a single light switch? Let's take switch twenty-four. Look at all the ways we could multiply two numbers to get twenty-four. There's 1 x 24, 2 x 12, and 3 x 4. That's a total of six times that the 24th switch gets flipped. And since it starts off, it would be off at the end."

"Any prime number only has two factors, one and itself, so all of those would be off as well," you add.

"Right. The lights which are still on at the end would just be those with an odd number of factors."

DAMAGE

You clear away some of the blocks from the low table to give yourself enough space to sit while you think about the poem in the picture book. After reading through several times, you're still not sure what you're supposed to do. "Hey, David, do you have any ideas on this poem?"

He shoves aside more blocks and takes a seat next to you. "I don't believe the actual words hold the answer. I think we need to get down to the individual letters. Maybe we have to pick out a few letters, and they'll tell us what the answer is."

"But how do I know which letters to choose?"

He shrugs. "Just try stuff."

Hints

DEEP

"I don't really want to go in there except as a last resort," David says when he notices you standing next to the 'Employees Only' door.

"But it is," you remark. "We've opened every other lock we've come across. Every one except for this. If only there was a clue as to what the combo is."

"Maybe there is!" David says, his face lighting up. "What about this?" He pulls out the Buddha statue which had been in the restroom.

"What are we supposed to do with it, throw it at the door?"

He laughs. "I assume there's a more elegant solution. We also haven't used that quote we found in non-fiction. Maybe they work together somehow."

EFFECT

After spending some time scribbling on the nonogram, David says, "I think this is all I'm going to get out of the puzzle."

"I don't get it," you admit. "Don't nonograms usually make a picture of something? Every time I try to solve it, I get the same jumbled mess. It doesn't look like anything."

"It's not supposed to. It's a decoder. We'll need something else like a grid of letters, and the nonogram will let us know which letters to use and which to throw out. We need to find another piece in order to solve it."

"Oh, I forgot about the decoder part."

You'll need another item from the children's section in order to solve this puzzle.

FINISH

The books are in pretty rough shape, and a few of the characters in the titles are difficult to make out.

"Clearly the missing numbers will give us the combination for the lock," David says. He turns the number dial then pulls on the lock, but it doesn't budge. "Did I get one of them wrong?" He peers at the books for a moment before glancing back down at the lock. "No, this is definitely right."

"Maybe the order is wrong," you suggest.

"But what order should the books be in?" You glance around the mess that is the fiction section, recalling these books' lack of organization. Perhaps whatever method typically used to arrange books could also apply to this case.

GASP

"We can't solve this until we get the other half," you say as you examine the torn piece of paper.

"I think we should double-check the third puzzle in the Cup of Joe book. We might need whatever object we got for solving that puzzle."

Once you have both sides of the torn paper, you'll be able to solve this puzzle. If you need another hint, look under the keyword ripped. The solution and conclusion are both under the keyword gasp.

GIVE

You examine the page you found in the tote at the new-releases area. "These characters look familiar."

"Oh, yeah. It's a pretty well-known cipher called pigpen. I should have a reference in my backpack." David pulls out a book of codes and opens it to a page with grids and numbers. "Just match up the shape with the letter." You hand him the paper and he starts marking it with a pencil. "The first one is an M, then the next two are both P, and then an L—"

"That's not a word," you point out.

"No, it's not." He furrows his brow and looks from the secret message to his book and back.

An idea pops up in your mind. "I bet it's not pigpen, but it might be something similar."

"Right, we did find something that looked like pigpen in the cash box," he says. He pulls the sheet from his bag and works on decrypting the message one more time. "It works! The message says: *Look at back.*"

Hints

KNIFE

You suspect that the shelf with only two titles will give you the combination to the locked bag, but you're not sure exactly how. David has also been staring at the bookcase for a while. "We need a three-digit code, and there are three rows. Maybe we convert the books into binary. Have the black books represent 1 and the white books be 0."

You shake your head. "I like that idea, but then the numbers would be too big. An eight-digit number in binary is pretty large. Look at the third row. If it were 11000000 in binary, that's $2^7 + 2^6$ which is one hundred ninety-two."

"Then let's try something different. What if we break it up into sections of six books?" He gestures at the first two columns of books. "This could be the first section, then the next two columns the second."

"That would give us four sections. We need a three-digit code."

"Yes, but maybe one of those is a symbol, like a pound sign."

You cross your arms. "Okay, let me keep thinking about it."

LEMON

David takes the logic puzzle and clues you found out of his backpack and spreads them out on one of the café tables. "I love this type of problem. Don't mind if I take a whack at it, do you?"

"Go ahead," you say as you sit down at the same table. You're curious to see how this puzzle works.

"So every person has a favorite number, each of which has a place in the combination for a lock. Let me look at this clue first: *Alice's favorite number is a factor of the digit that is first in the combo.*" He begins placing Xs in the grid. "Alice's favorite number could be two or three since those are factors of six. Two is also a factor of eight. So Alice's number can't be six or eight." He draws an X in the row labeled Alice in the squares which are next to the digits six and eight. "I'll put a circle in the spot that denotes her favorite number."

"Is that all the information you can get from that clue?" you ask.

He smiles, "No. We also know that the first digit in the combo is a composite number since Alice's number is a factor. Therefore, the first digit is not two or three." He marks down two more Xs.

"So that's everything?"

"Nope, there's still more! We know that Alice does not know the first digit, so we can cross that off as well."

"And *now* we're done with the clue," you say.

"Well, no. If we later learn that the first digit of the code is eight, then Alice's favorite number would have to be two since this clue tells us it's a factor. Similarly, if we learn that Alice's favorite number is three, then the first digit would have to be six."

Hints

NOISE

"So, we'll need three liters to fill the first beaker, then that will flow to the four-liter beaker—"

"Wait," you interject, not fully confident with David's plan. "What about gravity?"

He scratches his chin. "Oh! Right! Once the water gets up to that fourth tick, it will start getting diverted to the next beaker. That one won't fill up enough for water to ever go to the one on the far right. Let me think about this a little more and I might have an answer."

NUANCE

"How do we get up there?" you ask as you look up at the second-floor mezzanine.

"Those stairs are the only way up," David says, pointing to the walled-off area next to the register. "The door is locked, but we've gotten some clues to open it. Remember the puzzle we picked out from that logic problems magazine and those two clues we found? I think those will get us in."

You will need the Logic Puzzle from solving Periodicals and both logic puzzle clues: one from solving the New Releases and the other from solving the fiction puzzle.

If you need another hint, look up the keyword lemon. The solution and conclusion for the stairs will still be under the keyword nuance.

PIGEON

"This clue is incredibly vague," you announce.

"I think that's the point," David says. "It's the owner's password hint. It probably only makes sense to him."

You turn the tablet so it's facing you and have your fingers poised to start typing. "All right, I'm just going to put in a few guesses. Let me try *The Great Gatsby*."

"Stop that," David says as he pushes your hand away. "There are millions of book titles. It'd be pretty much impossible for us to guess the right one."

"Then what are we supposed to do?" you ask.

"Let's keep looking around," he suggests. "The owner's favorite book is probably also in this store. I bet we can find a copy of it somewhere."

You sigh. He has a point. You'll need to keep looking around the main floor, and then you can come back to the tablet when you have a better idea.

You will need to solve the fiction puzzle first.

POSTURE

"This page looks so weird," you say. "Why is the exclamation point so big?"

David takes a seat at the cluttered table and you do the same. "Let me see that again." He studies the page for a moment, then recites the message aloud. "I don't think reading it reveals anything, but the T in blurt is different from the other Ts."

"Wait, did you hold on to that tea bag we found in the café cabinet?"

"I think so." He looks through his backpack, finally locating the small item in the side pocket. "Should we soak the paper in tea? There could be some special ink that might show up."

"No, it looks like just normal ink on normal paper."

He smooths down the page with his hand. "There may be some other way to use the tea."

PROOF

"This triangle puzzle is so easy. A is forty-five degrees, B is one-eighty, C is forty-five, and D is ninety. But there isn't a key with those numbers on it."

"Maybe you should convert it to radians," David suggests.

"And get fractions of pi? No. All these keys have three-digit numbers."

You hand the keyring to David, and he looks at a few of the keys while examining the numbers engraved on them. "Have you tried adding the angles?" he asks. When you shake your head no, he says, "I don't see a key labeled three hundred sixty. Two pi is about six point two eight. Let me try key six twenty-eight." He walks over to the leftmost cabinet and shoves the corresponding key into the lock. The key, however, won't turn.

"There must be something else we're missing," you say.

"Maybe it's a code, and the angles themselves are the characters. I think I have a reference in my backpack that might help."

RIPPED

You pair the two torn pages together to see what you get. "Where is I?" you say, reading the second question. "That's some terrible grammar."

David points at one of the words on the page. "Unless it's referring to the letter I. Then it's correct."

Upon closer inspection, you realize that every word is nine letters long and contains three instances of I. That can't be a coincidence.

After double-checking that the number of squares in the grid is the same as what the text says, you admit, "I have no idea where to even start for this one."

"Hmmm," David says. "I'm trying to recall everything I learned in geometry class in high school."

"I don't think this is geometry since all we're doing is counting. Maybe I should just draw a ten-by-twelve grid and manually count all the squares—"

"No," he interjects. "There must be a better way. Let's be smart about this. How do we get the number of one-by-one squares?" He lays the puzzle page on the café counter, then grabs a pencil and blank paper from inside his backpack.

"It's just the number of rows times the number of columns."

He writes down *10 x 12* on his paper. "Now how many two-by-two squares." He looks at you, and you shrug. "Think about only the top-right corner. That corner could be just about anywhere, except the left column and bottom row. If we put a two-by-two square in those spots, it would hang out beyond the grid. So, we need to subtract one from the number of columns and number of rows.." He then writes *9 x 11* on the paper. "We just need to keep going until we get the biggest square which will fit."

STEM

David has flipped the Cup of Joe booklet to its back and studies the diagram. "Remind me what the area of a circle is," he says. Even though he's smart, he sometimes has trouble with geometry.

"Pi R squared, where R is the radius," you answer.

"Right," he mumbles.

You sigh, waiting for him to continue. After silently staring at the puzzle for a few more minutes, you say, "So, do we need to find the distances between the centers to calculate the area of the overlapping region?"

"No, I think the only thing we have to compute is the actual area of the circles. We won't need anything more complicated than that."

WARNING

After studying the list on the sticky note you found in the new-releases area for a while, you're still not sure what it means. "What are we supposed to do with this?" you ask, mostly to yourself.

David glances at it, then says, "It lists sections in the bookstore. We should go back to each one and take a closer look. Maybe there's something in each place that stands out or makes those areas unique."

Solutions

ANNUAL

After David fiddles with his calculator for several minutes, he finally says, "I think I've got them all. We already said the kilometer one is *20,000 Leagues Under the Sea*. The one below it is 7.41 fortnights. A fortnight is fourteen days, so multiply 7.41 by 14 to get 80 days."

"*Around the World in 80 Days*. That was one of the old books in the case," you point out.

"Right. Next, find out how many days 24,024 hours are. A day has twenty-four hours, so divide 24,024 by 24 to get 1,001 days. And every day has a night, giving us *1,001 Arabian Nights*. And finally, if you convert 232.78 Celcius into Fahrenheit—"

"Let me guess," you interrupt. "It's *Fahrenheit 451*."

"That's correct. Now, what do we do with these book titles?"

"What happens if you put them in the expression we were given?" you ask. "Divide 80 into 20,000. That gives 250. Add 1,001 to get 1251. Then you take away 451, which results in 800. That's a nice, round number."

David tucks his calculator back into his backpack. "Let's try it out on the lock."

BIKE

David pulls out a pen from his backpack and starts marking on the note. "Let's just look at the capital letters."

CoDeX fIX
CDXIX

"These five letters make a number if we read them as roman numerals."

You smack a hand on your forehead. Now that David said it, the clue is incredibly obvious. "Right. C stands for 100, D for 500, X is 10, and I means 1."

"Yep," he confirms. "And since the C is before the D, that means subtract 100 from 500 to get 400. Then XIX is 19, which gives us the solution of 419."

CARBON

You stand against the rail where you have a good view of all three signs. "I can't figure out how to make a code with these."

"I can show you my idea," David says as he pulls out a marker. He goes to each sign and underlines part of each word.

R<u>uno</u>logy S<u>cinco</u>id En<u>dos</u>cope

You cross your arms. "Uno, cinco, dos. That's Spanish for one, five, two."

He smiles as he replaces the cap on his marker. "I bet that's our code."

COMEDY

"What are we supposed to look at the back of?" David asks. Before you can suggest something, he continues, "I bet there's something hidden on the back of one of these books."

He starts pulling random books off the shelves and examining the back covers. But you already have a book in your hands, one that David isn't aware of. You flip your book over and look at the back cover. There's a logo for the publisher and a website, and under the website are three faint numbers. "The answer is two, four, four."

"How'd you get that?" David asks.

You simply shrug. "Try it. It'll work."

CONVICT

You've been alone in the bathroom for a while when David knocks on the door. "Are you okay in there?"

"Yeah, I'm fine, just thinking about this riddle. You can come in."

He enters the bathroom and joins you in staring at the sign above the light switch. "So every number that's prime or has an even number of divisors would be off at the end."

"What numbers have an odd number of divisors?" you ask.

"Only perfect squares. For example, eighty-one can be broken down to 1 x 81, 3 x 27, and 9 x 9. Nine is there twice since eighty-one is nine squared, but it's only one factor. Therefore, eighty-one has five factors and the eighty-first switch would be left on."

"Oh. Then we need the highest perfect square which is less than 1000."

You start multiplying numbers in your head, but David interrupts your thoughts. "Thirty-one squared is 961, so that must be our answer."

DAMAGE

After a few more minutes, you almost have the kitten poem memorized.

"It's an acrostic," David says. "Take a look at the first letter of each line."

You look at the page with fresh understanding. "I didn't even notice," you say. "It spells out *last letters*." You examine the lines again, this time focusing on the final letter. The odd number of lines makes sense if you're trying to hide a message with a certain number of characters. "The answer is seven, one, two."

Deep

As you're examining the Buddha statue, David says, "I've got an idea. Let me see that." He takes the quote you found and holds the statue in front of it. "Look. See how the statue blocks most of the quote, and there's only a few characters visible in the void between his arm and body?"

You carefully align the page with the quote behind the statue so the two horizontal lines align with the top of the statue's legs. Between the Buddha's body and arm you can see the O in "only," the first S in "mistakes," and the G in "along."

"Something is wrong with that G," you remark.

"I know. It looks almost like an eight, doesn't it?"

"It does!" You look again at the three isolated letters. They could also be read as numbers. "It's zero, five, eight."

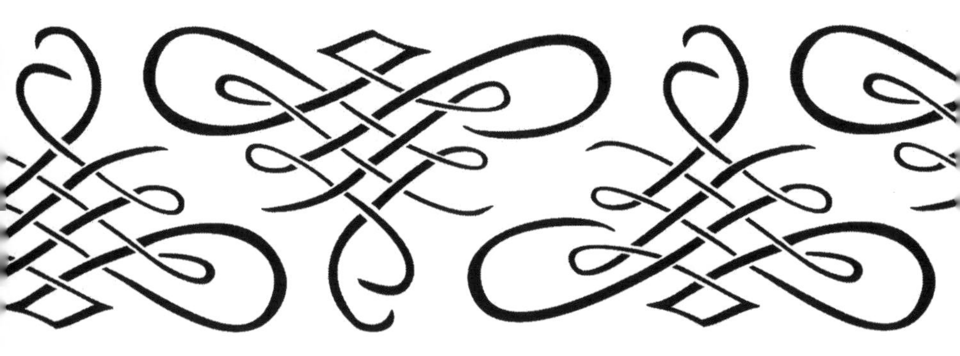

There are
only two
mistakes one can make
along the road to truth.
Not going all the way,
and not starting.

EFFECT

David used a pencil from his backpack to shade in the nonogram. "This is what I get."

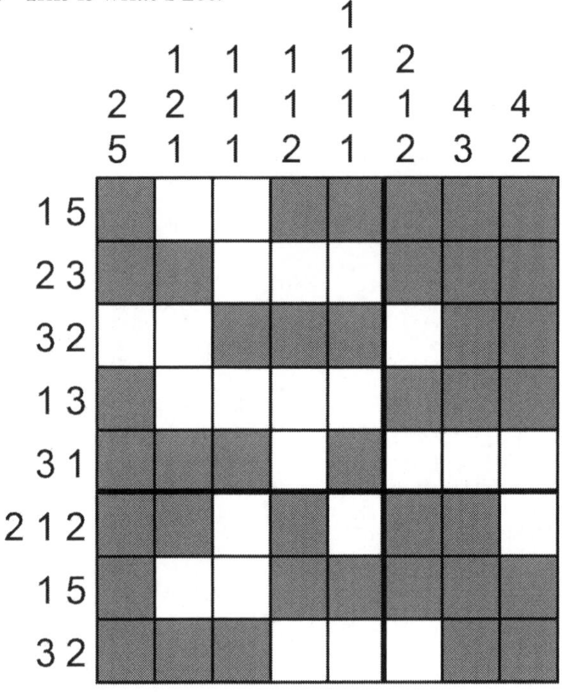

You look at his solution, and it seems to work. "But what now? It has to decode something."

He removes the word search you found in the children's section from his backpack. "Look at what happens when we place the letters from the word search into the nonogram."

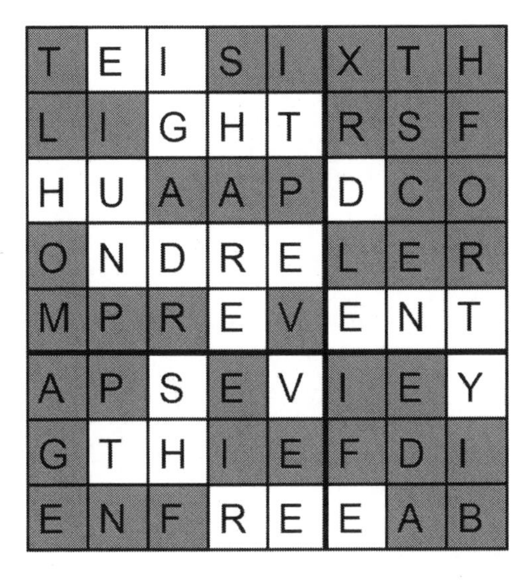

T E I S I X T H
L I G H T R S F
H U A A P D C O
O N D R E L E R
M P R E V E N T
A P S E V I E Y
G T H I E F D I
E N F R E E A B

After examining it for a moment, you see the words snaking through the white spaces. "Eight hundred seventy-three."

FINISH

In non-fiction, all the books on a certain topic get grouped together, but fiction is never that easy—especially when the owner hasn't even bothered to break up the collection by genre.

"We should alphabetize them by author name," David says. "So do Clark first, then Orwell, and then Verne."

"All right. So our order is 2001: A Space Odyssey, 1984, Around the World in 80 Days. And the digits which were missing were one, eight, and eight."

GASP

You hand the two halves of the paper to David and say, “I see several of the letter I in this puzzle, but I’m not sure what to do with them.”

“Well, the first question asks Where am I. The only word in the list which is also a place is Virginias.”

“So, either Virginia or West Virginia?”

He gives you a sideways glance before continuing. “In the word Virginias, which places have the letter I?”

“The second, fifth, and seventh.”

David gives you a hearty pat on the back. “That’s our code: two, five, seven.”

KNIFE

"I've figured it out," David declares, gesturing at the shelf of new releases. "It's braille. The black books represent raised dots."

He pulls out a book from his backpack and turns to a page with the Braille alphabet. "See, the first character is a pound symbol. After that, the next character is a one."

You notice that the character for **A** and **1** are the same in braille, but the pound symbol indicates that it's a number. That explains why there were four characters in the code instead of three.

"The second is a two, and the last is zero."

NOISE

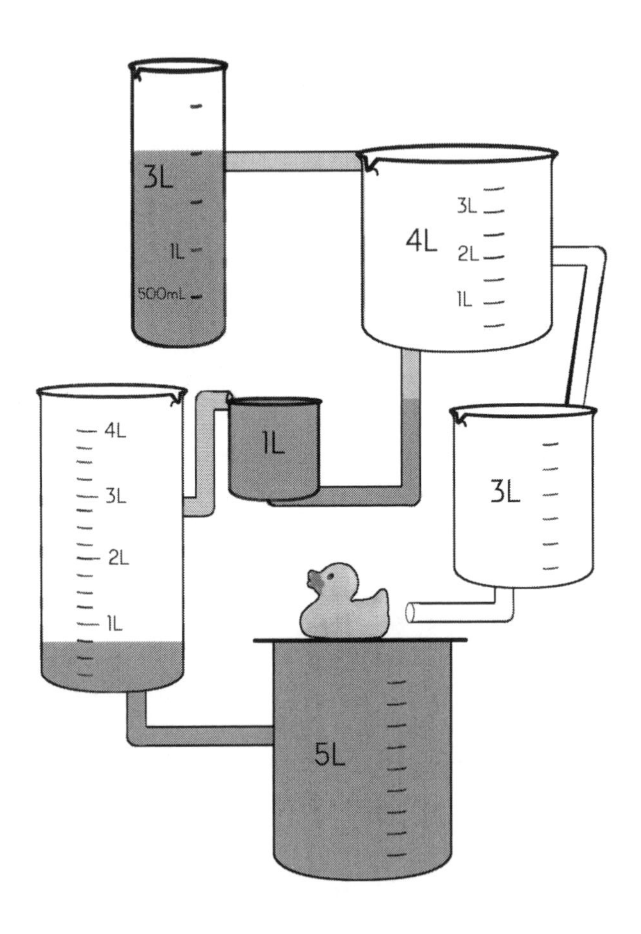

David takes the jug to the sink and begins to fill it with water while he explains the solution he came up with. "The first beaker will fill up until it reaches two liters. At that point, the water will start diverting to the 4L beaker. No water collects in the 4L beaker since there's a pipe on the very bottom. The little 1L beaker has to fill all the way up before water spills out of that one to the tall beaker on the left. From there, the final beaker with the duck starts filling.

"Except, the level at the top of the duck beaker is higher than the bottom of the beaker on the left. The water level will want to stay at the same height on both, so when the duck beaker reaches full, the left beaker will have 750mL inside. Add all those volumes together, and you get 8.75 liters."

"That's a lot."

He lets out a short laugh. "Yeah. You should grab another jug."

NUANCE

David holds up the logic puzzle and says, "This may take a while to explain, so get comfortable."

Instead of settling in, you're at the edge of your seat. "So what's the answer?"

"From the first clue, we know that Dan's digit is either 1st or 2nd in the combo and that his number is 2 or 3. The second clue tells us that the 1st digit is 6 or 8. However, Dan's number can't be 6 or 8, so he's not the 1st digit. This means his must be the 2nd.

"The first clue lets us know that the third digit is larger than two other numbers, therefore it must be 6 or 8. From the first clue, we know that Alice has either 2 or 3, so Alice is not 3rd in the combination. We already said Dan is 2nd and Alice is not 1st, so her favorite number is not in the combo.

"From the first clue, we know the number not in the combination is not the biggest or smallest number. It must be 3 since we already know Alice had either 2 or 3. The second clue told us her number is a factor of the first number, so the 1st number must be 6.

"Like Alice, Dan was also either 2 or 3. Since Alice has 3, he must have 2.

"The only number left is 8, and the only position remaining is 3rd, therefore 8 is the 3rd digit."

"So which number is Carol's favorite?" you ask.

He shakes his head. "We don't need that information. We've already paired all the digits and places. The 1st number is 6, the 2nd is Dan's number , 2, the 3rd is 8, and the digit not in the code is Alice's, which is 3."

"That gives us the code six, two, eight," you state.

"Yes, that's what I said—just in fewer words."

PIGEON

"Of course!" David exclaims. "I know what the owner's favorite book is!" You wait patiently for him to explain whatever epiphany he's had. "You know that book we found disguised as *Around the World in 80 Days* in the rare bookcase at the back of the fiction section?"

"Yes, the one by Ray Bradbury."

"That must be the owner's favorite book."

"Great. Remind me what the title was."

"Think about it" David says. "All the codes are three-digit numbers. Bradbury wrote a book with a three-digit number in the title."

"Oh, right," you say. "*Fahrenheit 451*. So the password is 451."

"Precisely!"

Solutions

"The message and the tea must be connected," you say.

"I think I know how," David says, smiling with excitement. "Replace the T with tea."

"I don't follow."

He turns the page so you can see it, and then places the tea bag next to it. "Replace the T in blurt with the name of the tea."

"*You must blur* From a Distance *out the message*. Oh, wow, that gives it a totally different meaning."

"Yeah! Let's do it." He gets up from the table, and both of you leave the employees only room and go to the mezzanine, where you have more space. After giving the page a quarter turn to the right, he says, "Can you make out what it's supposed to be?"

You squint in order to make the page appear blurry. "Wow, I see the code! It's one one seven."

PROOF

"Here it is," David says as he pulls a book out from within his backpack. He flips through it, and once he finds a specific page, he lays it open on the counter so both of you can read it.

"Semaphore?" you ask.

"It's a code using flags. If you pretend the point is the person and the two lines are their arms, then you can decipher the angles."

"Oh, I see. And the first angle gives us the number sign, so the following three must give the digits."

David is already carefully studying the figures. "I got it. The answer is four, seven, nine."

SET

"I get four hundred ninety-five," David announces.

"Can I see how you got that?" you ask.

"Sure." He hands you the paper with all of his notes.

Size of square	Number of them in grid		
1 x 1	10 x 12	=	120
2 x 2	9 x 11	=	99
3 x 3	8 x 10	=	80
4 x 4	7 x 9	=	63
5 x 5	6 x 8	=	48
6 x 6	5 x 7	=	35
7 x 7	4 x 6	=	24
8 x 8	3 x 5	=	15
9 x 9	2 x 4	=	8
10 x 10	1 x 3	=	3
	Total		495

"Wow. That's a lot of squares."

David nods. "Yeah, aren't you glad we decided not to count them individually?"

"That would have taken forever," you say with a laugh.

STEM

Suddenly, David shouts, "I've got it!"

You clasp your hands over your ears. "Ouch, give me some warning next time you're going to start yelling.

"Sorry... but I figured out the answer to the circle puzzle."

"How did you do it?"

He starts copying down the diagram onto a fresh sheet of paper as he explains his answer.

"Call the area of the striped region B. So what's the area of the dotted region?"

"It's also B," you say.

"Yes, but we can write it a different way. Call the radius of the big circle C. Now, take the area of the big circle, which is $C2\pi$. We only want the dotted area, so subtract the areas of the smaller two circles."

"Wait. The smaller circles aren't contained inside the big one, so you can't do that."

He gives you a smirk. "Yes I can—but I need to add back the area of those smaller circles outside of the big circle, and that area is exactly the striped region. So put it all together to get..." He writes down a sting of equations:

$$B = C^2\pi - 400^2\pi - 300^2\pi + B$$
$$B = C^2\pi - 1600\pi - 900\pi + B$$
$$0 = C^2\pi - 2500\pi$$
$$C^2\pi = 2500\pi$$
$$C^2 = 2500$$
$$C = 500$$

"The radius of the big square is 500 units."

"Wow, that's neat. I can't believe I didn't think of that."

After grabbing the rubber ducky from the counter, he tosses it to you and says, "Why don't you open this cabinet?"

WARNING

David has done a thorough search of the fiction shelves, the periodicals section, and the table holding the register. "I don't understand what the clue wants. I must be missing something."

You realize that there is a detail which sets these areas apart—specifically a really large letter. "What's it called when a new chapter starts with a big letter which takes up multiple lines?"

"A drop-cap. Why?"

"That must be it!" you exclaim. "Both the register and fiction sections start with an **I**, and periodicals starts with an **A**."

David raises a brow. "Okay. I'm not sure how you got letters for those sections, but **A** is the first letter and **I** is the ninth, so my guess would be nine, one, nine from what you've said."

"Let's go with that!"

Conclusion

ANNUAL

You carefully put your answer into the tiny number dials of the lock holding the journal closed and say, "You know, we also could have torn apart the cover."

David solemnly shakes his head. "Sacrilege."

The lock pops off and you open the journal. There's something written on the first page, and the rest appears to be blank. "Let's hold on to this page," you say.

You're about to rip out the page, but David grabs your arm. "What do you think you're doing? Don't tear pages out of books. I'll hold on to the journal."

Honestly, you see no harm in removing a page or two. But since you don't have to carry it, you won't fuss about it this time.

You find Journal Page.

BIKE

When you put in the combo to the cash drawer, it unlocks with a satisfying click. The drawer smoothly pulls out, revealing a handful of small bills and change.

"We should probably leave the cash in there," David says, peering over your shoulder. You weren't going to take any of it—there's something else in the drawer which has already caught your eye.

There's a folded note tucked in the tight space between the tray that holds all the money and the backside of the drawer. You fish out the paper and place it on the desk. After another quick inspection of the cash drawer, you determine there's nothing else important inside, so you lock it back up.

David takes the note and spreads it out, revealing another puzzle. "This must give us the password for the tablet."

You agree. "Let's figure it out."

You find Password Hint.

CARBON

You're able to get the lock off of the cash box and open it to see what's inside. "It's another note," you say, pulling out the slip of paper.

"It's a cipher," David responds.

"Right." You pull out the other object from the cash box, a small canvas zipper bag that requires a combination to unlock the zipper. "I bet there's yet another puzzle in here."

"You're probably right."

You find Pigpen Cipher.

COMEDY

David grabs the zipper bag that had been hidden in the cash-box and asks, "What was the code you came up with again."

You repeat your answer, and he turns each of the tiny number dials until the lock pops up, freeing the zipper pull. The zipper gets stuck a few times as he tries to open the bag, but he's able to get it open just enough to reach a hand inside. He pulls out a piece of paper and looks at it closely. "It's some sort of poem."

He hands you the paper and you read the text. "This isn't a poem," you say. "It's a quote from Buddha."

You find Buddha Quote.

CONVICT

Once you've input the combination into the lock, it falls off the cabinet. You open the doors and pull out the little statue. There's no slip of paper under it or insignia on the bottom. David peers inside the cabinet. "I don't see anything else interesting," he declares before closing it back up.

"What do you think this is for?" you ask, showing him the statue.

"I don't know, but let's hold on to it." He takes the object from you and places it in his backpack.

You find Odd Statue.

DAMAGE

You show David the activity book you found earlier. "I think this is where we use the code we got from the picture book."

"But it only has 365 activities. The number we found is larger than that."

Opening the book reveals that the activities aren't simply numbered, but that each one is also labeled with a different day. "Yes, but seven one two could also indicate July 12th."

The activity for that day doesn't stand out at all. Perhaps that's the point. "I'm not sure how a word search will help," David says, "But I'll hold on to it." He takes the whole book and places it in his backpack.

You find Word Search.

DEEP

You have to press each number on the metal keypad firmly in order for it to make a satisfying click. Once you input the last number, you press hard on the pound symbol and the door unlocks. The hinges groan as you push the door open.

You may now continue to the Employees Only area.

EFFECT

Now that you have an answer to the puzzle, you're not sure what to do with it. There are no locks in the periodicals section that require a combination. Perhaps the answer will unlock the door to the stairs which lead to the second floor.

You rush over to the locked door next to the register and press your number into the keypad, but nothing happens. "Drat. Now what?"

David follows you to the register and speaks up, "I have an idea."

"Sure, what is it?"

He leads you back to the periodicals. "The owner must be a huge fan of logic puzzles, right? I bet the clue is in this." He points to a book which has more pages—at least a thousand—than any other books you've seen.

"*Megabook of Logic Problems,*" you say, reading off the title. "What are we supposed to do with it?"

He opens it and flips to a particular page near the back. "Look at this." He points at puzzle eight hundred seventy-three. It appears to be like any other logic problem, except someone has made notes in pencil. "It's titled 'Combo to the Locked Door.' I bet this will literally open the door to the mezzanine."

"That's great!" you exclaim. You notice it doesn't seem to have any clues, but there could be more clues to solving it elsewhere in the store.

You find Logic Puzzle Page.

FINISH

"That was a pretty straightforward puzzle," you say as you fiddle with the lock to put in the combo.

David lets out a heavy sigh. "Just open it."

You unlatch the lock and set it down, then carefully slide one of the glass panels to the side. You each remove one of the books and begin to leaf through the pages. The copy of Clarke's *2001: A Space Odyssey* in your hands feels delicate and dry. You can smell the age of the pages. It isn't a first edition, but it clearly has some value.

David removes *Around the World in 80 Days* from the case, opens it, then says, "Hey, look at this." He hands the book to you, and you notice that the cover isn't attached. Inside is the text for a different book.

"Ray Bradbury," you say, reading the author name from the title page. "I wonder why this book was hidden."

"Maybe the owner didn't actually want to sell it."

"It's just a paperback, though," you point out. "And it's missing the original cover. I doubt it would sell for much money."

David takes the book from you and wraps it back in the other cover before returning it to its spot in the case. "It's probably special to the owner. But more importantly, I found this inside *1984*."

You look at the journal which had been hidden inside the classic dystopian novel. On the back appears to be another puzzle.

You find Locked Journal.

GASP

David approaches the little jewelry box, carefully puts your answer in the tiny lock, and then slowly opens the lid. It's the kind that has a little dancer figure that twirls while it plays music. You recognize the tune, *You are my Sunshine*, which starts at a quick pace, but eventually slows down to a crawl and finally stops.

"I think my sister had one just like this when we were kids," he says.

"Almost every girl did." You get closer to the box and look inside. There's a square of paper that's been folded up. "What's this?"

David pulls it out and examines it. "Looks useful. I'll hold on to it."

You get Confusing Cipher.

KNIFE

David picks up the tote. “Let’s see what’s inside.” You watch as he fiddles with the lock and removes it. The zipper makes a satisfying *zzzzzt* sound as he opens the bag. “I only see a single piece of paper.”

“Like blank paper, or is there something on it?”

“Take a look.” He hands you the page, then flips the bag upside down and gives it a good shake. Nothing else falls out.

You glance over the paper. “Hmmm, interesting.”

You find Interesting Paper.

NOISE

"Let me help," you say as you watch David carry a very full pitcher of water to the beaker array in the café. You grab a second pitcher and carefully fill it right to the mark you know will lift the rubber duck out of the bottom tank without causing a spill. Once David has emptied his pitcher into the top, you do the same.

As the water flows down, it eventually reaches the very bottom, which causes the duck to slowly rise. When the last few drops settle and the water is just at the top edge, David grabs the duck and pulls it out, then says, "This has a lot more keys than I expected. It's going to take forever to figure out which one opens which cabinet. I'm sorry—this was a total waste of time."

"Don't dismiss it so quickly," you say. You hold out your hand and he passes you the duck. It's been a while since you've owned one yourself. The rubber ducky is pretty cute, but you're surprised it was buoyant enough to float while weighed down by the attached keyring. There must be hundreds of tiny keys on it. Each one has a number engraved on it. When you turn over the duck, you notice something written in black marker on the bottom. "Hey, check this out."

He reads the inscription aloud: "Drawer to right of the sink." He looks at you, his eyes wide, and says, "I totally forgot to check any of the drawers." Within a minute, he raced to the drawer, opened it, grabbed the contents, and ran back to you. "This must be the clue for which keys open the cabinets!" he says, holding up a booklet.

"That's great, but maybe we should check all the drawers before we dive into that."

“Right!” He sets the booklet down and systematically goes through the café, checking every drawer and pulling every cabinet door. There’s only one other drawer, and it’s full of napkins. “All clear,” he says. “Now let’s look at that booklet!”

You find Cup of Joe

NUANCE

David stands at the door to the stairs and says, “Why don’t you put in your answer?”

You carefully punch in each digit on the keypad, ending in the pound sign. The lock makes a metallic tink as it comes undone. David pulls the door open and starts climbing up to the second level with you close behind.

You may now continue to the Second Floor.

PIGEON

David watches as you type the passcode on the tablet. It unlocks to show a menu. There's an icon for the checkout app, inventory management app, and email. You open the email app. Unfortunately, there doesn't seem to be any network the tablet can connect to, otherwise, you'd send out a message for help. There is a single message in the inbox. "Should we read his email?" you ask.

"Normally I'd say no, but these are special circumstances."

You tap the subject line for the email and turn the tablet so David can read it with you.

To: Athena Booksellers
From: BuildingOwner@MainStreet.com
Subject: Past Due

The rent for 43 Main Street is past due. If the rent is not paid IN FULL by next Wednesday, I will be forced to start the eviction process on your bookstore.

Craig Elliot
Area Manager
Main Street Property Management

You glance at David then back at the tablet. “This doesn't look good at all.” The bookstore is one of his favorite places, and he looks positively distressed.

“There's no way Athena Booksellers is having trouble paying their lease. It's *always* crowded here.”

“It doesn't matter how crowded it is if no one's buying anything,” you point out. David's expression saddens, though is seems he knows you're right. This bookstore has been fairly busy every other time you've visited, but most of the patrons were sitting in the café working while nursing a single cup of coffee. You haven't paid close attention to the register, but considering how disorganized the shelves are, you doubt people are buying much.

“We need to do something to help them.”

“I'm more concerned with getting out of here,” you say. Both of you have been trapped for a while now, and it doesn't feel like you're any closer to finding the combination to the front door.

David pokes at the tablet for a minute longer before he declares, “I don't think we're getting any more information from this thing. Let's move on.”

POSTURE

You've figured out the answer, but are unsure where to input it. There's nothing locked inside the small employee area. Then you remember that there's one last lock to open—the one on the front door.

"Let's see if this code gets us out of here," you say. You lead the way back around the non-fiction section, down to the main floor, and to the entrance.

"You do the honors," David says. "It is your birthday, after all." In all the excitement of finding a way out of this bookstore, you had almost forgotten about your hopes for a surprise party. If there really was one, you've probably missed it by now.

You spin each dial of the lock, and once you have the numbers aligned, it unlatches. You pull it off the chain and unwind the metal links from around the doorknob. With a hard shove, the door swings open, and you and your friend are able to walk outside. The air is thick and humid, but also a bit chilly. The rain has let up for the moment, but you suspect more is on the way.

You're about to walk down the sidewalk and back home, but then you notice a woman wearing a khaki trench coat running toward the bookstore. "Oh my goodness, were you two locked inside?"

Continue reading under the keyword zebra in the conclusion section.

Thankfully, the number you have in mind as the answer corresponds to one of the keys on the ring. "Let's try this key on the left-most cabinet," you say.

David takes the key from you and pushes it into the lock. It turns smoothly, and the cabinet opens. "Wow, this is a lot of tea."

The cabinet is filled with boxes and boxes of different teas, ranging from flavored black teas to herbal blends. You're about to dismiss the cabinet for having nothing useful when you notice a locked tea box with a note stuck on top. "What's that?" you ask.

"I bet it's another puzzle."

You find Wet Torn Paper

SET

David almost misses the key for the second cabinet and has to go through the entire keyring on the rubber ducky twice before finding the right one. Once he has the correct key, he puts it in the lock of the middle cabinet, turns it, then swings open the door. Inside are stacks and stacks of mugs. "See anything useful?" he asks.

You look as closely as you can at all the mugs, but none of them stand out.

"Here it is," he announces, pointing to a bit of paper taped on the inside of the door.

"Great! Go ahead and grab it, and then let's keep looking around."

He pulls the paper off the cabinet door and puts it in his backpack before locking the cabinet back up.

You find Taped Clue.

STEM

Fortunately, the first key you check is the one engraved with your answer. You put it in the rightmost of the three cabinets, and with a little wiggling, you're able to get the door open. "It's empty."

"Are you sure?" David asks.

"Oh, there's a torn paper sitting on the shelf." When your hand brushed the paper, you feel something else deeper in the cabinet. You grab the other object and pull it out. "It looks like a jewelry box."

David takes the paper from you, then says, "Maybe we

should leave the box there."

After examining the darkly stained wood box, you say, "It's got a lock, and it's not very heavy. I doubt there's anything of value inside."

He crosses his arms and lets out a huff. "Fine. Let's just leave it on the counter." After examining the torn paper for a few seconds, he adds, "I bet there's another half."

"Probably," you say as you close the cabinet and lock it back up.

You find Torn Paper.

WARNING

You place the locked tea box on the café bar and carefully turn the little lock until it clicks open. You gingerly lift the top, excited to see what's inside. At the bottom of the box is a single bag of tea.

"Oh," David says as he slumps his shoulders. "I was hoping this thing contained something more exciting."

"It could be a super special tea..."

"No, I know this brand. It's nothing special."

You remove the tea bag from the box and examine it closely. "This particular tea had to be locked up for a reason. I'm confident it contains a clue."

"Fine, I'll hold on to it." He takes the little square of tea and shoves it in the side pocket of his backpack.

You find Tea Bag

ZEBRA

You glance from the pretty young woman to David. He answers, "Yes, we *just* figured out the combo to the lock and got out."

"I'm so sorry. You two weren't meant to get locked inside—I was! Please, come back inside out of the rain and I'll explain everything."

"Sure," David says, gesturing for you to come as well.

Once inside, the woman says, "Please take a seat and I'll make some tea."

You and David sit down at a table in the café, and within a minute, the woman comes over and sets down a tray holding three steaming mugs of hot water and an assortment of teas. David grabs a mint tea bag and plops it in a mug while you select an herbal chai tea.

Satisfied, the woman takes a seat as well. "I'm not sure if you know the owner of this bookstore, but I'm his niece, Skylar. I guess my friend wanted to set up a puzzle hunt for me for my birthday, so she worked it out with my uncle to do it in his bookstore."

"That explains a lot!" David says. "And happy birthday! Today's actually my friend's birthday, too."

She chuckles, then smiles at you. "Well, I hope you enjoyed my birthday surprise! I was supposed to do it tonight, but I got stuck in traffic with the storm. When I called my friend, I told her to go ahead and lock up, but she forgot to check that everyone had left first. I didn't even think about it until I was almost here. I should have told her to make sure the place was empty—what a terrible mistake."

David says, "Your friend put together some great

puzzles. I really like the nonogram which had to be paired with—"

"Wait," you interject. "Instead of telling her what the puzzles were, why don't we reset everything so Skylar can go solve them all?"

"Only if it's not too much trouble," she says. But you can tell by the gleam in her eye that she's excited.

David taps his chin. "Actually, yeah, that's a good idea. I used a pencil when I wrote things down, so I can erase everything we wrote on the papers."

Both of you get up from your seats, and only a few minutes later, the puzzle hunt is reset and ready for a new player.

Before you say your goodbyes to Skylar, you're still bothered by one little detail. After David tells her everything is all set, you suddenly blurt out, "There was one puzzle that doesn't go anywhere, so I'm not really spoiling anything, but when we unlocked the tablet for the register, we were able to read one of your uncle's emails."

"Oh, the point-of-sale machine? The password is just four-five-one, after my uncle's favorite book."

David adds, "I think your uncle is having trouble paying his lease. His landlord sent him a pretty threatening email."

"Oh, Craig." She rolls her eyes. "He's quite dramatic. He's not great at keeping records and sends out those messages just about every month. So every month, my uncle sends Craig a copy of the canceled check for that month's rent."

"Oh, wow. That's great to hear." David lets out a sigh. "This bookstore is just about my favorite place, and I would hate for it to close for real."

Skylar grabs her coat and puts it back on. "I'll have to pass that on to my uncle. He'll be pleased to hear how much you like it here. Well, it's getting late. I should close up this place for the night and get home. I'll have to solve my birthday surprise tomorrow."

You nod in agreement, and the three of you go back outside. Skylar locks the door behind you. The rain has finally stopped. "It was a pleasure meeting you," you tell Skylar. "And happy birthday."

"Same to you!" She waves, and then continues walking down the sidewalk to where her car is parallel parked.

You and David walk the few blocks back to David's car and he drives you straight home. "So, no surprise party?" you ask.

"I already told you, no."

By the way he smiles, you're still not sure you should believe him. As soon as you open your front door, a sweet puppy comes bounding at you, its tail wagging. It covers you with doggie kisses as you give it a hug. "Molly! I can't believe you're here!" The puppy you had bonded with at a local rescue hadn't been ready for adoption when you visited last week, and you didn't think you'd be able to adopt her for at least another month.

"I was able to get the rescue to rush her paperwork, and Camilla picked up Molly and brought her here while we were out. On that note, she's been cooped up for a while. You should probably take her out for a walk."

"This is the best birthday ever!" you gush, giving your friend a big hug. "Thanks so much."

He smiles broadly. "You're welcome, buddy."

THE END

Answer
Check

HOW TO CHECK YOU ANSWERS

Find your answer in the following table. Next to it is a cell address for table 2. If the word in the corresponding cell matches the keyword for the puzzle you're checking, you have found the correct answer!

000	Q3	020	C4	040	E5	060	B6
001	E3	021	F1	041	E1	061	K6
002	T3	022	U6	042	L9	062	P2
003	T3	023	G7	043	S2	063	K9
004	I5	024	D2	044	B2	064	P8
005	J5	025	P5	045	Z6	065	E4
006	H5	026	Z8	046	B8	066	B8
007	H4	027	X1	047	Z7	067	Y2
008	E1	028	X8	048	O5	068	N5
009	S9	029	E8	049	A5	069	J5
010	N4	030	D3	050	G5	070	B9
011	S3	031	S1	051	H8	071	H5
012	M5	032	V7	052	A8	072	P6
013	N6	033	R2	053	L2	073	V8
014	L8	034	Z3	054	H5	074	Y7
015	Z9	035	T9	055	P3	075	N5
016	L4	036	D4	056	S9	076	B5
017	C2	037	K5	057	B3	077	N2
018	Z4	038	S1	058	P9	078	B3
019	A6	039	T3	059	J6	079	Z3

080 I3
081 T2
082 A9
083 Z4
084 C8
085 C6
086 Z1
087 L3
088 U7
089 V4
090 E2
091 Y6
092 E1
093 B6
094 N9
095 I6
096 C1
097 R1
098 I4
099 M1
100 T4
101 J9
102 L7
103 O7
104 R8
105 Q7
106 U7
107 T7
108 P9
109 Z9
110 A8
111 Q8
112 B3
113 D3
114 K3
115 T3
116 J6
117 U6
118 L8
119 Y1
120 T9
121 R5
122 G5
123 A6
124 C7
125 R9
126 C1
127 V1
128 L8
129 D2
130 I5
131 T5
132 F3
133 R3
134 U7
135 S9
136 S9
137 A9
138 I7
139 B3
140 C3
141 M1
142 Y4
143 G1
144 V9
145 I1
146 V4
147 T1
148 V5
149 L5
150 E2
151 L2
152 O9
153 I1
154 P7
155 K6
156 N4
157 O4
158 N9
159 S1
160 Q2
161 L3
162 B3
163 G7
164 S8
165 O7
166 B5
167 W8
168 T6
169 H4
170 H4
171 C6
172 J4
173 X1
174 T1
175 H9
176 O5
177 H3
178 I3
179 B9
180 O3
181 U9
182 O4
183 W5
184 W3
185 E7
186 S7
187 F1
188 M1
189 P1
190 H6
191 N6
192 Y8
193 D2
194 Q1
195 Y3
196 H4
197 I9
198 X5
199 M5
200 G5
201 D4
202 M5
203 F7
204 P5
205 M1
206 A8
207 B5

208	R8	240	K1	272	W6	304	Q7
209	H9	241	P4	273	S8	305	F5
210	A2	242	G3	274	K5	306	D1
211	G1	243	L3	275	D9	307	A3
212	Y2	244	N8	276	A8	308	T3
213	P3	245	U2	277	M6	309	E4
214	H8	246	W4	278	C3	310	I6
215	Q6	247	T1	279	Q4	311	L4
216	A4	248	U2	280	U3	312	R1
217	X8	249	X5	281	B7	313	J8
218	H8	250	K1	282	N8	314	S3
219	P9	251	H1	283	B7	315	K1
220	N9	252	Y9	284	T5	316	G1
221	J6	253	V8	285	S3	317	B5
222	N7	254	Z7	286	V1	318	L6
223	J6	255	X3	287	L5	319	J9
224	V2	256	Z6	288	U9	320	V6
225	V8	257	S2	289	N7	321	E9
226	F3	258	X8	290	D6	322	N3
227	Y5	259	X6	291	P6	323	W2
228	D7	260	Z5	292	X5	324	T5
229	G7	261	L4	293	X5	325	Q5
230	H7	262	A5	294	H9	326	A6
231	T9	263	R2	295	T6	327	H7
232	T8	264	A2	296	L6	328	F3
233	F9	265	P8	297	M9	329	E5
234	O5	266	H9	298	R6	330	E3
235	B7	267	P8	299	S3	331	X1
236	Y8	268	A5	300	C1	332	H1
237	T7	269	P7	301	T7	333	C4
238	B3	270	F4	302	P1	334	Y4
239	R1	271	Y4	303	D9	335	N9

336	O3	368	E2	400	E4	432	T4
337	C1	369	E7	401	O4	433	K5
338	Y5	370	C2	402	P9	434	K1
339	M1	371	G9	403	L1	435	J9
340	C2	372	O7	404	E4	436	C5
341	M4	373	M5	405	X7	437	Y1
342	L4	374	D2	406	G3	438	Y1
343	Z9	375	T6	407	S1	439	C8
344	O4	376	Y6	408	G5	440	S4
345	O4	377	E2	409	Z3	441	L1
346	S2	378	Q8	410	A7	442	E3
347	N2	379	K9	411	X2	443	U6
348	X4	380	Q7	412	O9	444	T9
349	D1	381	N5	413	D3	445	X6
350	M7	382	W8	414	Z2	446	G5
351	K4	383	F5	415	F3	447	P3
352	N5	384	L7	416	A8	448	Y5
353	B4	385	S5	417	G6	449	R2
354	H8	386	A9	418	W3	450	S8
355	L4	387	Y1	419	O8	451	D8
356	F4	388	Q4	420	W5	452	L1
357	Z9	389	L4	421	V4	453	H5
358	V2	390	T3	422	D7	454	X8
359	Y8	391	K7	423	X7	455	W9
360	S4	392	Q7	424	V8	456	F2
361	K2	393	R7	425	N5	457	C8
362	Z4	394	D7	426	Q9	458	N6
363	F9	395	Y4	427	I7	459	M8
364	M6	396	K1	428	I6	460	F3
365	E9	397	V3	429	F1	461	B7
366	O5	398	T4	430	I5	462	O4
367	N8	399	Y1	431	Z8	463	A3

464	Z9	496	D6	528	K4	560	Z7
465	O6	497	T2	529	H1	561	A6
466	F8	498	H5	530	T9	562	Z4
467	C3	499	L8	531	K4	563	D7
468	T7	500	L5	532	E1	564	E2
469	U3	501	K9	533	S2	565	K8
470	I7	502	N9	534	E1	566	K4
471	R6	503	Z3	535	Q1	567	A3
472	H7	504	P8	536	T7	568	O4
473	N2	505	X7	537	H8	569	Q5
474	L5	506	N3	538	P4	570	Z6
475	L5	507	L9	539	Z5	571	U7
476	P9	508	I2	540	C2	572	N9
477	L2	509	K4	541	N7	573	U2
478	R8	510	L6	542	S1	574	E7
479	V2	511	L8	543	B4	575	U7
480	W3	512	C3	544	V2	576	Z1
481	J4	513	G2	545	W3	577	Z4
482	N7	514	U6	546	J6	578	U4
483	M3	515	J7	547	G2	579	N9
484	I7	516	W8	548	H6	580	Y1
485	B5	517	O3	549	R6	581	N7
486	S7	518	E4	550	U5	582	Z1
487	A7	519	C9	551	T9	583	M7
488	C5	520	I3	552	S7	584	O4
489	N3	521	Q1	553	F2	585	F7
490	J6	522	Z9	554	U4	586	W3
491	O1	523	A1	555	K3	587	I6
492	L8	524	R7	556	V5	588	W1
493	X9	525	O3	557	J9	589	M2
494	W7	526	O3	558	I8	590	D7
495	Q1	527	R8	559	K3	591	N8

592 Y1
593 N6
594 N6
595 F7
596 W6
597 Q8
598 J1
599 Y3
600 H8
601 O2
602 G8
603 C2
604 D7
605 T6
606 J3
607 S4
608 X5
609 A8
610 E1
611 A6
612 F4
613 F7
614 X1
615 Q7
616 R2
617 C9
618 Z9
619 M8
620 Y4
621 N7
622 A7
623 H1
624 Y1
625 K7
626 J1
627 C8
628 W3
629 B7
630 F7
631 W1
632 C2
633 K5
634 Y5
635 T2
636 Z4
637 E1
638 B9
639 F7
640 Z2
641 J3
642 L1
643 G5
644 Q2
645 W3
646 E9
647 X9
648 X4
649 E6
650 U3
651 Y3
652 E6
653 J2
654 G3
655 S5
656 Q1
657 V8
658 I8
659 L3
660 U3
661 W6
662 V6
663 H9
664 Y6
665 Q1
666 F3
667 M6
668 T9
669 Z3
670 I6
671 P1
672 E1
673 Z6
674 V9
675 U6
676 N1
677 D7
678 O2
679 I3
680 G7
681 E9
682 Z6
683 T6
684 H1
685 H8
686 T5
687 J4
688 C3
689 V3
690 L1
691 J7
692 Y4
693 O4
694 Q2
695 F4
696 B2
697 J5
698 Z9
699 Q2
700 M2
701 X3
702 T2
703 O9
704 S9
705 L1
706 M3
707 D2
708 H3
709 H6
710 D4
711 Z2
712 V7
713 J4
714 X9
715 L6
716 G6
717 Y8
718 B4
719 Q5

720 P9
721 R2
722 U1
723 N7
724 Q5
725 F2
726 Q6
727 Q1
728 J6
729 B2
730 G9
731 E2
732 X4
733 I3
734 N7
735 F4
736 C6
737 E5
738 O5
739 Z8
740 C6
741 Z4
742 Q3
743 N4
744 X2
745 E6
746 H6
747 B5
748 R7
749 S7
750 Q8
751 F1
752 S5
753 J2
754 J8
755 D9
756 L7
757 B6
758 R2
759 G9
760 R8
761 G4
762 K4
763 I8
764 W6
765 J3
766 O7
767 I6
768 Z6
769 M5
770 K3
771 L5
772 W7
773 X8
774 D9
775 O5
776 T9
777 Y4
778 E1
779 J6
780 K3
781 V3
782 V8
783 S2
784 P6
785 J6
786 V5
787 J6
788 G7
789 M4
790 W2
791 E9
792 M8
793 A1
794 R3
795 N3
796 O4
797 J9
798 I5
799 P5
800 V6
801 X6
802 X9
803 R3
804 G5
805 Z8
806 O1
807 Z9
808 H5
809 J6
810 U5
811 M9
812 X2
813 R4
814 Z2
815 L5
816 R4
817 G9
818 K6
819 P5
820 U9
821 O1
822 F7
823 C3
824 S4
825 F5
826 Z7
827 V8
828 S4
829 E1
830 Z9
831 Y2
832 X3
833 T1
834 F8
835 F4
836 T8
837 A5
838 D1
839 D2
840 C6
841 E1
842 U3
843 J4
844 Y4
845 V6
846 N5
847 P4

848	L9	867	W8	886	Z4	905	X6
849	V6	868	F6	887	N1	906	V9
850	D1	869	P4	888	S2	907	W8
851	V4	870	H5	889	W5	908	M8
852	B7	871	M7	890	J4	909	I6
853	B6	872	A6	891	D5	910	B3
854	Y6	873	B1	892	Z8	911	H8
855	A5	874	V4	893	D5	912	C7
856	B4	875	L7	894	W6	913	I7
857	U2	876	B7	895	N5	914	S7
858	B5	877	S4	896	C5	915	I8
859	F5	878	H2	897	T4	916	P1
860	N4	879	E9	898	O7	917	L5
861	J5	880	R9	899	P3	918	I7
862	W5	881	D4	900	Z6	919	J5
863	D4	882	R6	901	P7	920	C1
864	N6	883	D6	902	D5	921	X7
865	D1	884	C7	903	W5	922	H4
866	U8	885	Q3	904	U2	923	M7

924 V2
925 D1
926 H2
927 I3
928 P4
929 L4
930 L8
931 B8
932 R6
933 H7
934 M4
935 Q3
936 J7
937 Z4
938 Z7
939 N9
940 I7
941 O9
942 B6
943 X1
944 D1
945 Y1
946 M2
947 E4
948 V8
949 X9
950 Q1
951 O6
952 H1
953 L9
954 O9
955 K4
956 N3
957 H2
958 J5
959 D3
960 P7
961 I5
962 D1
963 H7
964 O9
965 U3
966 D6
967 L5
968 A2
969 V2
970 Q5
971 F6
972 J9
973 I1
974 E4
975 M2
976 I7
977 Z5
978 F5
979 G1
980 S9
981 M6
982 J5
983 Q8
984 C8
985 B6
986 R4
987 I6
988 O4
989 R3
990 O1
991 V1
992 W9
993 S9
994 F3
995 D4
996 S1
997 U4
998 W3
999 Q9

TABLE 2

	1	2	3	4
A	health	horror	coffin	climb
B	effect	paint	reality	differ
C	splurge	curtain	theory	soldier
D	culture	extinct	like	rotate
E	happen	coach	cake	field
F	freedom	report	tracker	honor
G	seat	expand	hover	ring
H	loud	doll	healthy	confine
I	dozen	scale	stumble	variant
J	throat	speech	cry	get
K	joint	century	shorts	ecstasy
L	supply	ideal	aisle	twitch
M	finish	comfort	justice	scratch
N	fox	relocate	hike	debate
O	dash	card	plant	youth
P	enhance	partner	trench	stroke
Q	set	exclude	union	soft
R	mutter	pig	blank	chair
S	bundle	gasp	go	yard
T	hostage	shark	flu	lover
U	liberty	suffer	decay	burn
V	waste	proof	singer	slow
W	immune	keep	nuance	grant
X	war	diagram	traffic	weigh
Y	bat	north	unique	output
Z	painter	public	horse	item

5	6	7	8	9
path	weight	bare	eat	tree
dish	colon	session	facade	virtue
banana	grace	tick	runner	couple
fold	glass	sit	pigeon	present
color	mud	certain	pray	lamb
shadow	amber	ready	tract	sigh
raw	grip	blade	slip	forge
ride	volcano	wriggle	tough	create
convict	module	switch	sing	sense
warning	animal	attack	banner	vat
thumb	blow	ankle	stake	breathe
stem	good	noise	cancel	Bible
ethics	track	cancer	active	drug
exotic	labour	unit	comedy	goal
storm	model	burial	bike	carbon
welcome	storage	crew	dome	deep
creep	corn	glance	offset	half
seal	prefer	menu	gaffe	college
clothes	bean	cluster	swell	crack
waiter	fossil	attic	relax	knife
pattern	posture	crouch	express	frank
history	annual	damage	hay	tune
dice	affair	penalty	resign	mystery
screw	hut	bargain	favour	maze
recycle	powder	mute	bitter	out
rumor	percent	round	include	mayor

Objects

HOW TO USE THESE OBJECTS

Whenever you find an object, simply tear out the corresponding page in this section. You can keep track of the objects you have found by keeping them together in the front or back of this book. Some objects may go together or require physical manipulation to figure out.

BUDDHA QUOTE

There are
only two
mistakes one can make
along the road to truth:
Not going all the way,
and not starting.

CONFUSING CIPHER

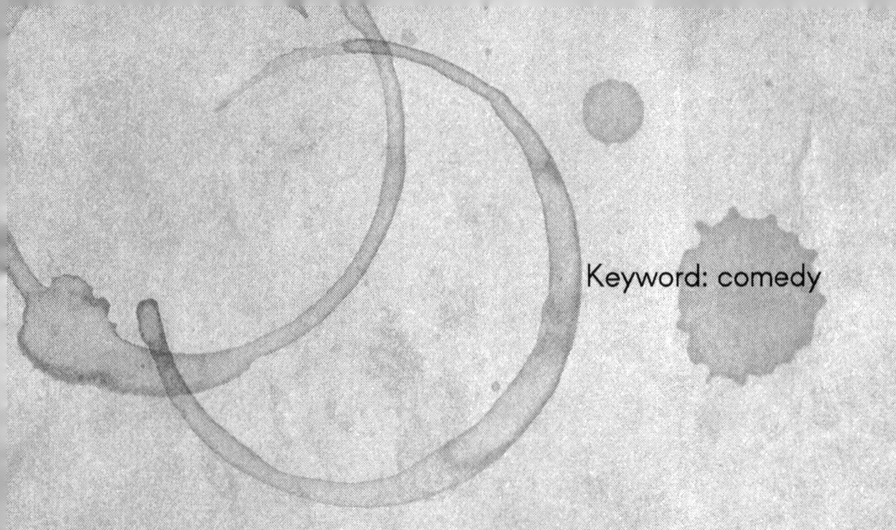

Keyword: comedy

CIRCLE

Keyword: stem

There are three circles. The area of the striped region is the same as the dotted region.

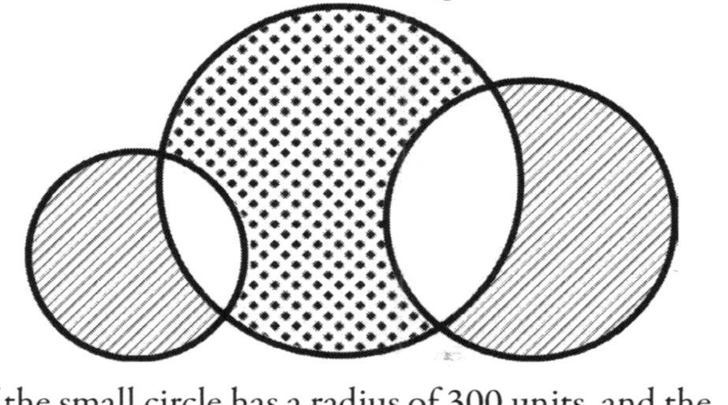

If the small circle has a radius of 300 units, and the medium circle has a radius of 400 units, what is the radius of the large circle?

Cup of Joe

CUP OF JOE

TRIANGLE

Keyword: proof

ABC is an isosceles right triangle. What are the angles?

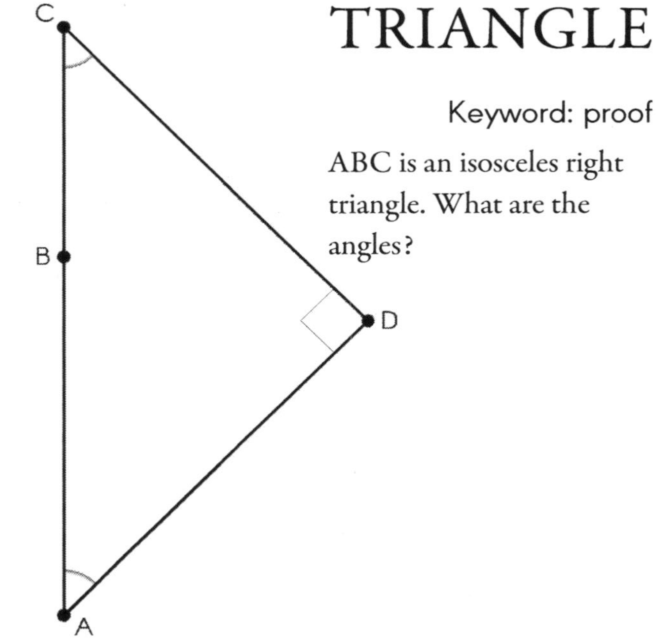

SQUARE

Keyword: set

This 3 x 3 grid contains fourteen squares: nine 1 x 1 squares, four 2 x 2 squares, and one 3 x 3 square.

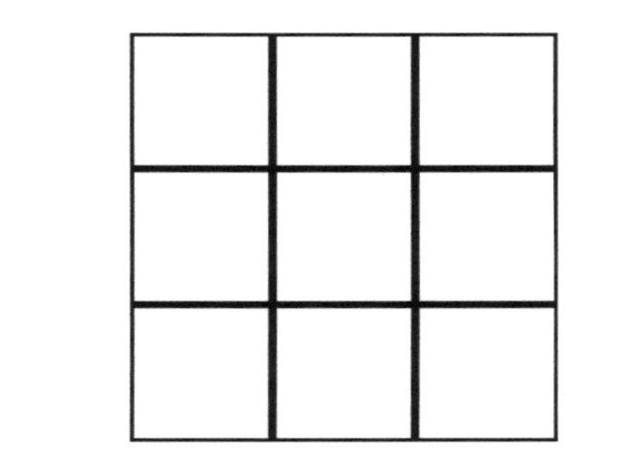

How many squares are in a 10 x 12 grid?

DECODER FOR UPPER-LEVEL KEY

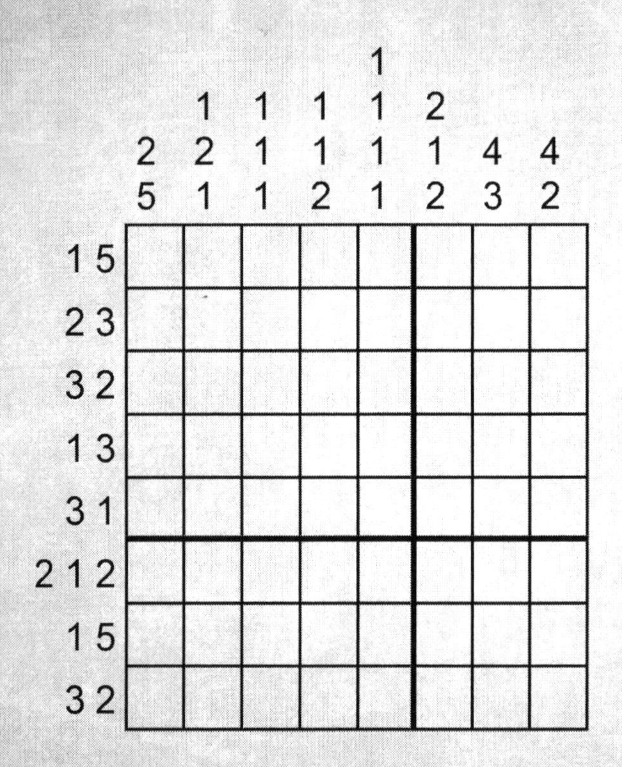
2 5
1 2 1
1 1 1
1 1 2
1 1 1 1
2 1 2
4 3
4 2
1 5
2 3
3 2
1 3
3 1
2 1 2
1 5
3 2

INTERESTING PAPER

Keyword: warning

Fiction Periodicals Register

JOURNAL PAGE

Clue 1

1. The friend whose number is not in the combination has a larger favorite number than Dan's, but smaller than the person whose digit is third in the combo.

LOCKED JOURNAL

Keyword: annual
96,561 km
5.71 fortnights
+ 24024 hours - 232.78 celcius

LOGIC PUZZLE PAGE

Combo to Locked Door

	2	3	6	8	1st	2nd	3rd	none
Alice								
Bob								
Carol								
Dan								
1st								
2nd								
3rd								
none								

ODD STATUE

PASSWORD HINT

Keyword: pigeon

My favorite book.

PIGPEN CIPHER

I bet this cipher will be confusing!

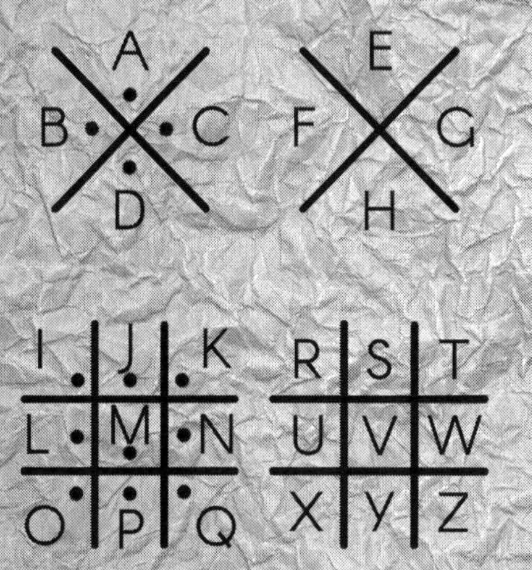

TAPED CLUE

Objects

Clue 2

2. Alice's favorite number is a factor of the first digit in the combination.

TEA BAG

Celestial Tea
HERBAL BLEND
From a
Distance

TORN PAPER

Where am I?

DIETITION DIVISIBLE

IMITATION INHIBITOR

KIWIFRUIT LIQUIDITY

WET TORN PAPER

MINISKIRT SINUS-

ITIS

WHIRLIGIG VIRGINIAS

Where is I?

Keyword: gasp

WORD SEARCH

T	E	I	S	I	X	T	H	LIGHT
L	I	G	H	T	R	S	F	PREVENT
H	U	A	A	P	D	C	O	SHARE
O	N	D	R	E	L	E	R	SCENE
M	P	R	E	V	E	N	T	FORTY
A	P	S	E	V	I	E	Y	FREE
G	T	H	I	E	F	D	I	HOMAGE
E	N	F	R	E	E	A	B	THIEF

DAVID

BINARY

In mathematics and digital electronics, a binary number is a number expressed in the base-2 numeral system or binary numeral system, which uses only two symbols—typically 0 and 1.

In the binary system, each digit represents an increasing power of 2, with the rightmost digit representing 2^0, the next representing 2^1, then 2^2, and so on. The equivalent decimal representation of a binary number is the sum of the powers of 2 times the digit in each place. For example, the binary number 100101 is converted to decimal form as follows:

$$
\begin{aligned}
100101_2 \quad &= [\,(1) \times 2^5\,] \\
&+ [\,(0) \times 2^4\,] \\
&+ [\,(0) \times 2^3\,] \\
&+ [\,(1) \times 2^2\,] \\
&+ [\,(0) \times 2^1\,] \\
&+ [\,(1) \times 2^0\,] \\
\\
&= \;[\,1 \times 32\,] \\
&+ [\,0 \times 16\,] \\
&+ [\,0 \times 8\,] \\
&+ [\,1 \times 4\,] \\
&+ [\,0 \times 2\,] \\
&+ [\,1 \times 1\,] \\
\\
&= \;32 + 4 + 1 = 37_{10}
\end{aligned}
$$

BRAILLE

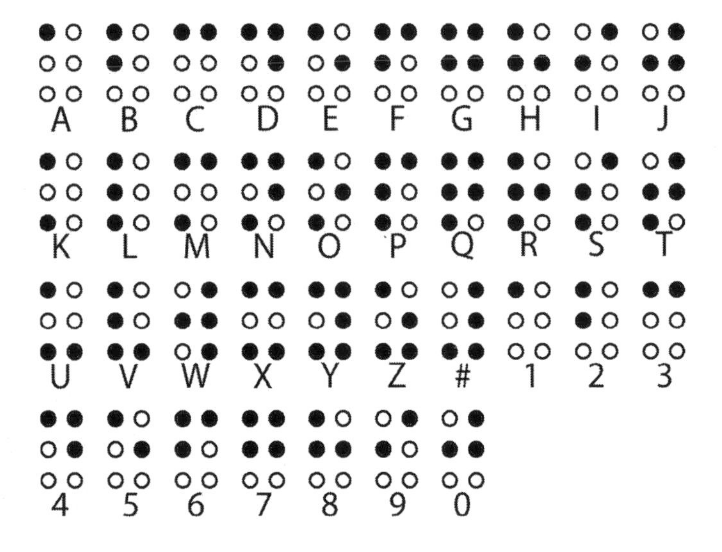

NUMBERS IN DIFFERENT LANGUAGES

	English	French	Spanish	German
1	one	un	uno	eins
2	two	deux	dos	zwei
3	three	trois	tres	drei
4	four	quatre	cuatro	vier
5	five	cinq	cinco	fünf
6	six	six	seis	sechs
7	seven	sept	siete	sieben
8	eight	huit	ocho	acht
9	nine	neuf	nueve	neun
10	ten	dix	diez	zehn

PIGPEN

Pigpen Cipher uses a grid of letters to convert text into a string of symbols. The key is easy to recreate, so any ciphertext in Pigpen Cipher is simple to decrypt.

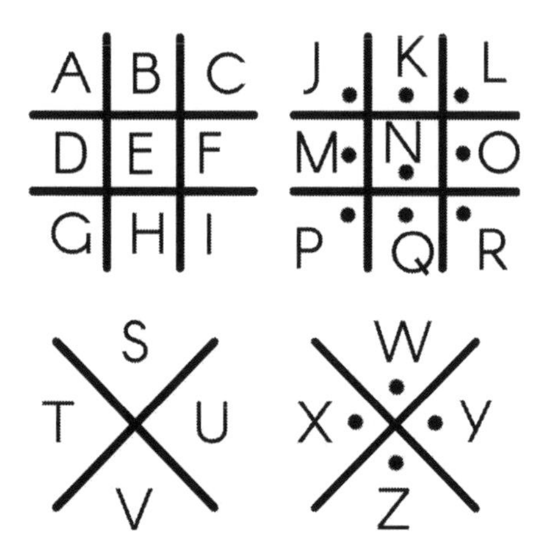

To encode a message, use the lines around each letter in the grid to create the symbol.

For example:

H E L L O W O R L D

gives:

ROMAN NUMERALS

I	V	X	L	C	D	M
1	5	10	50	100	500	1000

1 = I
2 = II
3 = III
4 = IV
5 = V
6 = VI
7 = VII
8 = VIII
9 = IX
10 = X

10 = X
20 = XX
30 =XXX
40 = XL
50 = L
60 = LX
70 = LXX
80 = LXXX
90 = XC
100 = C

XVII = 17
CMXI = 911
MDCCCIV = 1804
MMXX = 2020

SEMAPHORE

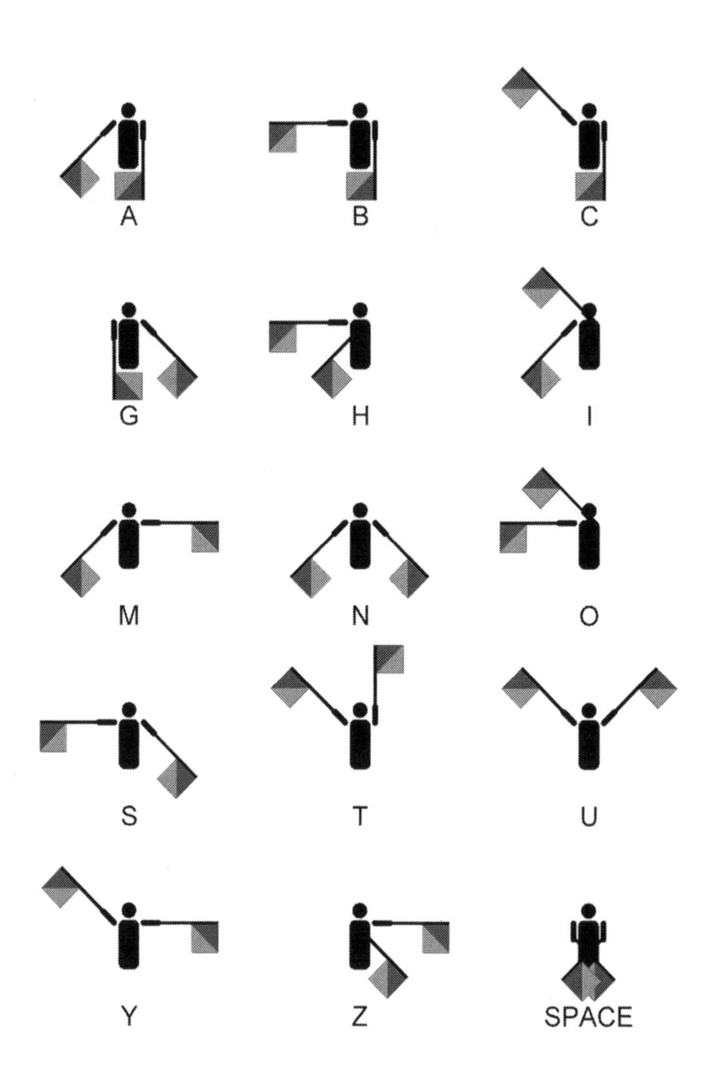

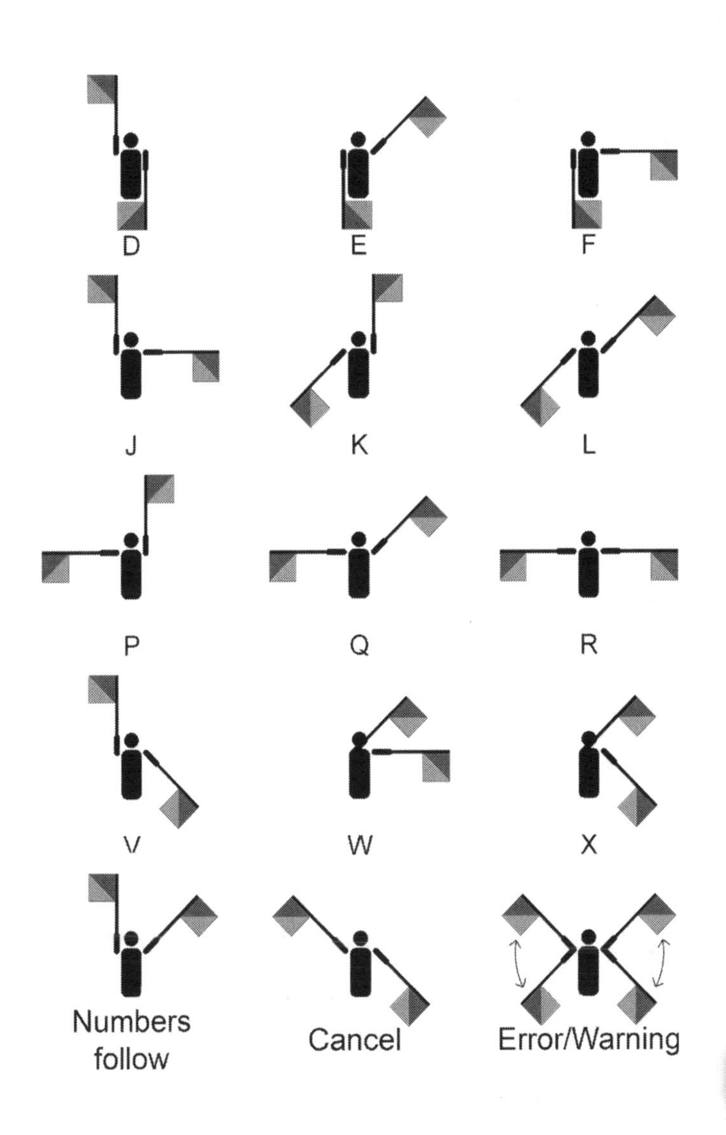
D
E
F
J
K
L
P
Q
R
V
W
X
Numbers follow
Cancel
Error/Warning

UNIT CONVERSION

Distances

12 inches = 1 foot
3 feet = 1 yard
5280 feet = 1 mile
3 miles = 1 league

10 mm = 1 cm
100 cm = 1 meter
1,000 meters = 1 Kilometer

1.609 Kilometer = 1 mile
2.54 cm = 1 inch

Temperature

Kelvin = Celsius +273
Fahrenheit =
(9/5) x Celsius + 32

Time

60 seconds = 1 minute
60 minutes = 1 hour
24 hours = 1 day
14 days = 1 fortnight
365 days = 1 year

Volume

1,000 mL = 1 Liter
3.79 Liters = 1 gallon
8 ounces = 1 cup
2 cups = 1 pint
2 pints = 1 quart
4 quarts = 1 gallon

ACKNOWLEDGEMENTS

Thanks so much for playing through *Puzzling Escapes: Trapped in the Bookstore*! If you enjoyed this book, please consider leaving a review on Amazon or Goodreads.

After I released the first *Puzzling Escapes* book, I was flattered by all the love and support it's gotten. My readers and fans are what really keep me going, and I give you all the biggest thanks from the depths of my heart.

I always have to commend my husband for all the help and support he's given me. All of the puzzles in this book were either crafted or tested by him.

Fortunately, I've been able to work with the same editor, Josiah Davis, for most of my writing career. He's done a superb job helping me polish this book.

I have to say thanks to my friends and family who are so supportive in my writing endeavors. There are too many to name everyone, but I have to mention my amazing parents and all the members of the Columbia Writers.

OTHER BOOKS BY BETH MARTIN

Puzzling Escapes

Mystery of the Spaceship and the Missing Crew
Return to the Cruise Ship from a Deserted Island
The Terrifying Haunted House on Mystery Lane

Science Fiction Novels

The End of Refuge
Quality DNA
Mental Contact
At Fault
In the Lurch
In the Midst (In the Lurch Book 2)

ABOUT THE AUTHOR

Beth Martin is a science fiction author. She has her degree in mathematics, enjoys all things numbers, and is always up for a board game. Other hobbies include playing the piano and sewing. Although she's terrible at video games, she loves watching her husband play.

Most of her time is spent chasing her two adorable children. She also has two fluffy cats.